THE MARIA THUN BIODYNAMIC CALENDAR

2014

The original biodynamic sowing and planting calendar
showing the optimum days for sowing, pruning and harvesting
various plant-crops, as well as for beekeeping

Created by
Maria and Matthias Thun

Floris Books

Compiled by Matthias Thun
and Christina Schmidt Rüdt
Translated by Bernard Jarman
Additional astronomical material
by Wolfgang Held and Christian Maclean

Published in German under the title *Aussaattage*
English edition published by Floris Books

British Library CIP Data available

ISBN 978-086315-996-1
ISSN: 2052-5761

Printed in Poland

Walter Thun, The Guardian, *oil, 1982, 68 x 98 cm*

The Guardian

As with most creative painters who go through different phases in life, we can see in Walter Thun's work how not only the style of his painting but also the choice of theme underwent a transformation.

While at art college in Erfurt, Walter Thun dedicated himself entirely to painting church murals. He was very keen to express his ideas and imagination on large wall spaces and this he did as a journeyman in the Cologne area towards the end of the 1930s. As a soldier during the war he came across many different landscapes and so developed a great interest in landscape painting.

After encountering anthroposophy it became possible for him to refine his observation skills, so that he saw a rock for instance not simply as a rock, or a tree as a tree. He began to see and then paint in such a way that his *experience* of what he saw was reflected in the picture.

In the last period of his life Walter Thun occupied himself very intensively with Rudolf Steiner's concept of evolution. For this he had a very good conversation partner in his wife Maria who had developed a deep understanding for this subject.

A whole series of pictures were painted that addressed the concepts of evolution, observations and experiences. Walter Thun succeeded, in so far as his newly-won knowledge permitted, in presenting two similar yet distinct groups of themes. On the one hand he focused strongly on the idea of human development and this became clearly manifest in his work. An example of this was his painting *Crossing to the Other Shore* that was published in the 2013 calendar.

In this year's painting *The Guardian* we see human figures but also what he had perceived and experienced while observing the rocks.

This painting can be allocated to the second thematic group of paintings, in which the human being, though indicated, perceives an aspect of world development.

If the observer remains within the space in which they outwardly finds themselves while looking at the picture, they will experience something of the evolution of the earth and mankind from the past through to the present. The gaze of those rock-beings transforms this time experience into a kind of enclosed space. It is then led over into the future via the sun-filled background to which the human figures are looking.

The Guardian is similar in style and approach to the painting published in last year's calendar and yet differs in that the 'guardian' becomes the 'protector' of the earth's evolutionary time stream.

Introduction

This is 52nd year of this calendar. We would like to remind our readers that the data given on the monthly pages as well as the results of research refers to the *astronomical* constellations and not the *astrological* signs. The astronomical constellations of the zodiac vary in size, and are what we can observe in the night sky. The astrological signs are equally spaced 30° segments which have little to do with what is actually visible in the sky. There is a diagram on page 10 to help those who may be confused when they compare it with other Moon calendars.

This year we have included in some reports from users of the calendar in various countries. This helps see how the cosmic rhythms that we refer to and report on are not only experienced here in Dexbach in central Germany but can be observed throughout the world. The reports this year come from Europe and from Egypt. We hope that next year we can include reports from other parts of the world too. The reports are of medical work, horticulture and agriculture, including research results and wine growing. Many thanks to the authors for supporting this effort.

Matthias K. Thun

France

Coraly Joly

It is with deep gratitude and respect that we remember Maria Thun as the one who inspired and then supported our daily work on our vineyard by the River Loire.

Maria Thun frequently travelled to France with her son Matthias during the 1980s in order to lend support to the farmers living here and enrich them with her wisdom.

In 1986 we were blessed with the opportunity of being able to welcome Maria Thun to our vineyard for the first time. After this she came every year to meet and exchange experiences with the farmers and vintners of western France and then answer their endless questions with warm-hearted yet focused patience.

Maria and Matthias Thun enjoyed visiting us. There were no language barriers in our French-German household. We made litres of the coffee that she so much loved to drink during the seminar breaks. The small twelfth-century Cistercian monastery sited on the estate regained its original function as a training centre.

It was a wonderful period of time and each visit provided renewed strength for the following twelve months.

There was so much we could learn from her for our daily lives – about the egg shells, which reduce the effect of radioactive rays and which are so valuable that they should be boiled on the stove and the enriched water used for making tea, coffee and soup. This was one of many recommendations duly noted down!

About forty years ago Maria Thun held the first conference for women farmers. It took place in Switzerland. She wanted women to be able to meet, exchange experiences and learn together. She felt that the farm women were often left out and that this time the farmer should stay at home and look after the children, farm, and household. The age of women is approaching, she would explain!

The conference quickly became international, and still takes place each November. It is well attended and is always in different places and in different countries.

What an amazing contribution to life. It is hard to find words to express it. It is balsam for our souls, our fields and our vineyards.

Response

Matthias Thun

I would like first of all to thank Coraly Joly most warmly for her comments.

France has always been a special country for us. Interest in our zodiac trials and their results started there very early on thanks to two personalities who learnt about our work and then disseminated it in the French language from their homes in the Vosges mountains. They were Jeanette Zimmermann and Harald Kabisch.

Harald Kabisch was consultant for biodynamic agriculture in both Bavaria

5

The vineyards of the Joly family [Virginie Joly]

and the Vosges region. He worked there together with Jeanette Zimmermann who was at that time actively developing the French Weleda company as well as supporting the small gardeners who sought to apply biodynamic and organic principles.

Harald Kabisch was a friend of our family and came regularly to observe Maria Thun's research. He was so taken by the results that he persuaded my mother to publish them in his gardening journal so that gardeners, growers and farmers might apply them.

The practical success of this gave my mother the courage to make her experiences more widely available to practitioners in a simplified form. That was over 52 years ago.

Soon afterwards Jeanette Zimmermann and the mother of Georges Paulus took the initiative to translate the *Calendar* into French.

The benefits experienced by those using the calendar were so great that the courses initially given by Maria Thun in the Vosges region were now presented all over France. This work was strongly supported by Michel Leclaire and Claude Monzies.

To start with, my mother concentrated purely on gardening and farming activities in her lectures. As her lecturing activity extended out into the country's heartlands and into the south, an increasing number of her listeners were wine growers who brought more specialist questions. In order to do them justice she began a series of seminars specifically for wine growers.

Nicolas Joly, his wife Coraly and Francois Bouchet were particularly engaged with this development. They organised several conferences and seminars with my mother and this led to an amazing number of wine producers working with the biodynamic approach and applying the results of her zodiac research. The results were so impressive that Nicolas Joly and Francois Bouchet decided to develop an advisory service. Nicolas Joly's consultancy work soon took him beyond the borders of France. He has since written about and published his experiences in book form, now translated into several languages.

This initiative led not only to more healthy vineyards but also enabled the wine to develop the nuances of flavour which had been so sought after in the past – reason enough for biodynamic methods to be taken up so strongly by wine growers.

Many a biodynamic farmer in Germany found it hard to understand why Maria Thun spent so much of her time advising wine growers. She always responded by saying that if beer can be improved by using biodynamic barley then surely it is possible to produce better wine from biodynamic vineyards. The success of biodynamic wine surely proves how correct she was.

WHEN WINE
TASTES BEST
2014

A Biodynamic Calendar
for Wine Drinkers

When Wine Tastes Best

Hilary Wright

Does the day on which you choose to drink a bottle of wine affect its flavour? For some years now our major supermarkets have thought so. Both Tesco and Marks & Spencer now only hold tastings for wine critics on days when, according to this calendar, the wines will be at their best. And between them these supermarkets sell a third of the wine drunk in the UK, so they are probably on to something — something it's time the rest of us found out about.

The best days to drink wine are Fruit and Flower days. *When Wine Tastes Best* will tell you when Fruit and Flower days, and other auspicious times, will come around this year. It doesn't mean you can't drink wine on other days, of course, but you might like to drink your best wines on a day that will show your prize purchase off to best advantage.

It doesn't matter whether you believe the theory behind this; after all, scientists once believed the Sun revolved around the Earth. What matters is trying it for yourself and seeing how well it works.

The above is from the Foreword to When Wine Tastes Best *which Floris Books produces annually as a result of hearing about the supermarkets' wine tastings.*

From Gardeners and Growers in the Czech Republic

The Maria Thun Biodynamic Calendar has been published in the Czech Republic by the association for organic agriculture PRO-BIO since 1995. The experiences of Czech gardeners were gathered by Andrea Vizinová.

Silvie Siblíková

I once undertook a little experiment. I grew some flowers in my garden for drying and picked them each day throughout the week. I hung them up to dry and grouped them in sequence on the wire so that I would know which flowers were hung up on the first day and which on the fifth. The flowers picked at Flower times were undoubtedly better and always kept longest. I had expected there to be some differences but not to such a great degree. Those which I had picked at Fruit times were not bad either but those from Root times shrivelled as they dried and developed brown edges, and were unusable for flower arranging.

Helena Hájková

I live in the countryside and have been working with the *Calendar* in my vegetable garden since 2004. It had been established in a kind of 'moon landscape' (for twenty years it was a huge uncared-for strawberry bed) that even a spade could not penetrate. For several years in succession we suffered plagues of flea beetle, slugs and cabbage white caterpillars which in the course of a few days destroyed the work of several months. I persisted ...

I can safely say that, thanks to Maria Thun, for several years now almost everything has been growing as if by itself and the root vegetables are particularly good.

Ludmila Slavíková

We prepared our new home and I created a garden. I set to work taking large numbers of cuttings, remembering the experience of propagating roses in my youth. I knew that I would have to write off about half of them which wouldn't take. I was shocked the first time I used the calendar and didn't even dare tell my friends of the result in case they thought I made it up: all of the cuttings had taken! Every year I successfully take cuttings of blackcurrant plants and distribute them among my friends and family, knowing that they will all grow.

Vlasta Dohnalová

The Maria Thun Biodynamic Calendar has been in my house since 2003. I have been following its recommendations regularly. I don't know whether it has become a habit but I find that I cannot sow or harvest any longer without referring to the *Calendar*.

I always sow the seeds of cabbage and savoy in seed trays under glass at Leaf times. If I can't manage it for some reason then I choose a Fruit time. I always have beautiful and strong plants. When planting them outdoors I choose the descending Moon period. The plants then grow strongly and I generally have a good harvest.

I sow tomatoes at Fruit times, re-pot them at Fruit times and plant them out again at Fruit times during the descending Moon (weather permitting). I don't wish to blow my own trumpet but my tomatoes are really wonderful and keep on growing till it freezes. Much of course also depends on watering and side shooting.

The greatest effect I have observed is when harvesting fruit and vegetables! If we pick apples according to the Calendar – Fruit times, ascending Moon – they are juicy and don't decay (we do of course have a good fruit cellar).

The same occurs with root vegetables harvested at Root times or, failing that, Fruit times, but in any case during the descending Moon and if possible after rain. The roots then keep for a long time, perhaps also thanks to our good, moist cellar (although roots used to decay there much more).

The same is true for carrots, Hamburg parsley and onions sown at Root times and harvested at Root times. The vegetables do not go rotten, onions hung up on strings keep for a long time and even in spring do not sprout too much. I always sow cucumbers at Fruit times and always have a good harvest.

We always plant potatoes at Root times and harvest them at Root times too (weather permitting). They keep until spring as though freshly harvested.

For lettuce I use Leaf times, and flowers I sow at Flower times, both with good results: fine lettuce heads and beautiful flowers.

Jiří Šebela

We often look at our *Calendar* several times a day – not in order to plan our work in the vineyard or orchard (for this it is sufficient to check it once or twice a week), but primarily to plan our wine tasting and when to open our wines. The natural, non-chemical, unadulterated biodynamic wines are always more connected with their surroundings, so we make a point of never opening them at Root times. We always prefer to choose Fruit or Flower times.

Radim Pešek

My wife always works with the *Calendar,* and I used to make light of it and never took it seriously. One year I grafted an apple rootstock and she advised me to wait a few days because the time wasn't suitable. Because of lack of time I did not follow her advice. The graft took and the plant grew and I was convinced she was wrong. By the autumn it had grown to about 30 cm (12 in) and I was satisfied. I undid the tape and was shocked to see it drop to the ground – it had simply not grown together with the rootstock.

I tried again the next year, this time using the calendar. The shoot grew and I removed the tape after two weeks. To my surprise it had completely grown together and grew wonderfully. This result inspired me to use the *Calendar* in my beekeeping work too. I was amazed how strong the colonies became and how the honey yield increased as a result.

Background to the calendar

The zodiac

The **zodiac** is a group of twelve constellations of stars which the Sun, Moon and all the planets pass on their circuits. The Sun's annual path always takes exactly the same line, called **ecliptic.** The Moon's and planets' paths vary slightly, sometimes above and sometimes below the ecliptic. The point at which their paths cross the ecliptic is called a **node** (☊ and ☋).

The angles between the Sun, Moon and planets are called **aspects.** In this calendar the most important is the 120° angle, or **trine.**

In this illustration the outer circle shows the varying sizes of the visible **constellations** of the **zodiac.** The dates on this outer circle are the days on which the Sun enters the constellation (this can change by one day because of leap years). The inner circle shows the divisions into equal sections of 30° corresponding to the **signs** used in astrology.

It is the constellations on which our observations are based, and which are used throughout this calendar.

The twelve constellations are grouped into four different types, each having three constellations at an angle of about 120°, or trine. About every nine days the Moon passes from one type, for instance Root, through the other types (Flower, Leaf and Fruit) and back to Root again.

Root

Leaf

Flower

Fruit/Seed

See page 15 for a key to the zodiac symbols

If a New Moon is at a node there is a solar eclipse, as the Moon is directly in front of the Sun, while a Full Moon at a node causes a lunar eclipse where the Earth's shadow falls on the Moon. If the Sun or Moon pass exactly in front of a planet, there is an occultation (☽). If Mercury or Venus pass exactly in front of the Sun, this is a transit (other planets cannot pass in front of the Sun).

Trines △ or ▲

The twelve constellations are grouped into four different types, each having three constellations at an angle of about 120°, or trine. About every nine days the Moon passes a similar region of forces.

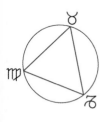

Earth-Root

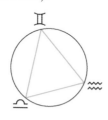

Light-Flower

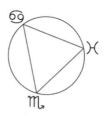

Water-Leaf

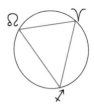

Warmth-Fruit/Seed

What are oppositions, trines and conjunctions?

Oppositions ☍

A *geocentric* (Earth-centred) opposition occurs when for the observer on the Earth there are two planets opposite one another — 180° apart — in the heavens. They look at one another from opposite sides of the sky and their light interpenetrates. Their rays fall on to the Earth and stimulate in a beneficial way the seeds that are being sown in that moment. In our trials we have found that seeds sown at times of opposition resulted in a higher yield of top quality crops.

With a *heliocentric* (Sun-centred) opposition an observer would need to place himself on the Sun. This is of course physically impossible but we can understand it through our thinking. The Sun is in the centre and the two planets placed 180° apart also gaze at each other but this time across the circle of the Sun's orbit. Their rays are also felt by the Earth and stimulate better plant growth. However, heliocentric oppositions are not shown in the calendar.

At times of opposition two zodiac constellations are also playing their part. If one planet is standing in a Warmth constellation, the second one will usually be in a Light constellation or vice versa. If one planet is in a Water constellation, the

11

other will usually be in an Earth one. (As the constellations are not equally sized, the point opposite may not always be in the opposite constellation.)

Trines △ or ▲

Trines occur when planets are 120° from one another. The two planets are then usually both standing in the same elemental configuration — Aries and Leo for example are both Warmth constellations. A Warmth trine means that the effects of these constellations will enhance fruit and seed formation in the plants sown at this time. If two planets are in trine position in Water, watery influences will be enhanced which usually brings high rainfall. Plants sown on these days will yield more leaf than those on other days. Trine effects can change the way plants grow.

Conjunctions ☌

Conjunctions and multiple conjunctions occur when two or more planets stand behind one another in space. It is then usually only the planet closest to the Earth that has any influence on plant growth. If this influence is stronger than that of the sidereal Moon, cosmic disturbances can occur that irritate the plant and cause checks in growth. This negative effect is increased further when the Moon or another planet stands directly in front of another — an occultation (•) or eclipse in the case of Sun and Moon. Sowing at these times will affect subsequent growth detrimentally and harm a plant's regenerative power.

The effects of the Moon

In its 27-day orbit round the Earth the Moon passes through the constellations of the zodiac and transmits forces to the Earth which affect the four elements: Earth, Light (Air), Water and Warmth (Fire). They in turn affect the four parts of the plant: the roots, the flower, the leaves and the fruit or seeds. The health and growth of a plant can therefore be stimulated by sowing, cultivating and harvesting it in tune with the cycles of the Moon.

These cosmic forces can also be harnessed in beekeeping. By opening and closing the bee 'skep' or box in rhythm with the Moon, the bees' activity can be directly affected.

The table opposite summarizes the effects of the movement of the Moon through the twelve constellations on plants, bees and the weather.

The amount of time the Moon spends in any constellation varies between two and four days. However, this basic framework can be disrupted by planetary oppositions which override the normal tendencies; equally, it may be that trine positions (see above) activate a different elemental force to the ones the Moon is transmitting. Times when the Moon's path or a planet's path intersects with the ecliptic (ascending ☊ or descending ☋ node; see previous page) are subject to mainly negative effects. These are intensified if there is an eclipse or occultation, in which case the nearer planet interrupts the influence of the distant one. Such days are unsuitable for sowing or harvesting.

Constellation	Sign		Element	Weather	Plant	Bees
Pisces, Fishes	♓	W	Water	Damp	Leaf	Making honey
Aries, Ram	♈	H	Warmth	Warm/hot	Fruit	Gathering nectar
Taurus, Bull	♉	E	Earth	Cool/cold	Root	Building comb
Gemini, Twins	♊	L	Light	Airy/bright	Flower	Gathering pollen
Cancer, Crab	♋	W	Water	Damp	Leaf	Making honey
Leo, Lion	♌	H	Warmth	Warm/hot	Fruit	Gathering nectar
Virgo, Virgin	♍	E	Earth	Cool/cold	Root	Building comb
Libra, Scales	♎	L	Light	Airy/bright	Flower	Gathering pollen
Scorpio, Scorpion	♏	W	Water	Damp	Leaf	Making honey
Sagittarius, Archer	♐	H	Warmth	Warm/hot	Fruit	Gathering nectar
Capricorn, Goat	♑	E	Earth	Cool/cold	Root	Building comb
Aquarius, Waterman	♒	L	Light	Airy/bright	Flower	Gathering pollen

Groupings of plants for sowing and harvesting

When we grow plants, different parts are cultivated for food. We can divide them into four groups.

Root crops at Root times

Radishes, swedes, sugar beet, beetroot, celeriac, carrot, scorzonera, etc. fall into the category of root plants. Potatoes and onions are included in this group too. Root times produce good yields and top storage quality for these crops.

Leaf plants at Leaf times

The cabbage family, lettuce, spinach, lambs lettuce, endive, parsley, leafy herbs and fodder plants are categorized as leaf plants. Leaf days are suitable for sowing and tending these plants but not for harvesting and storage. For this (as well as harvesting of cabbage for sauerkraut) Fruit and Flower times are recommended.

Flower plants at Flower times

These times are favourable for sowing and tending all kinds of flower plants but also for cultivating and spraying 501 (a biodynamic preparation) on oil-bearing plants such as linseed, rape, sunflower, etc. Cut flowers have the strongest scent and remain fresh for longer if cut at Flower times, and the mother plant will provide many new side shoots. If flowers for drying are harvested at Flower times they retain the most vivid colours. If cut at other times they soon lose their colour. Oil-bearing plants are best harvested at Flower times.

Fruit Plants at Fruit times

Plants which are cultivated for their fruit or seed belong to this category, including beans, peas, lentils, soya, maize, tomatoes, cucumber, pumpkin, courgettes, but also cereals for summer and winter crops.

Sowing oil-bearing plants at Fruit times provides the best yields of seeds. The best time for extraction of oil later on is at Flower times. Leo times are particularly suitable to grow good seed. Fruit plants are best harvested at Fruit times. They store well and their seeds provide good plants for next year. When storing fruit, also remember to choose the time of the ascending Moon.

There is always uncertainty as to which category some plants belong. Onions and beetroot provide a similar yield when sown at Root and Leaf times, but the keeping quality is best from Root times. Kohlrabi and cauliflowers belong to Leaf times, as does Florence fennel. Broccoli is more beautiful and firmer when sown at Flower times.

Explanations of the calendar pages

Next to the date is the constellation (and time of entry) in which the Moon is. This is the astronomical constellation, not the astrological sign (see page 10). The next column shows solar and lunar events.

A further column shows which element is dominant on that day (this is useful for beekeepers). Note **H** is used for warmth (heat). Sometimes there is a change during the day; in this case, both elements are mentioned. Warmth effects on thundery days are implied but are not mentioned in this column, but may have a ⁋ symbol in the far right 'Weather' column.

The next column shows in colour the part of the plant which will be enhanced by sowing or cultivation on that day. Numbers indicate times of day. On the extreme right, special events in nature are noted as well as anticipated weather changes which disturb or break up the overall weather pattern.

When parts of the plant are indicated that do not correspond to the Moon's position in the zodiac (often it is more than one part on the same day), it is not a mis-print, but takes account of other cosmic aspects which overrule the Moon-zodiac pattern and have an effect on a different part of the plant.

Unfavourable times are marked thus (- - -). These are caused by eclipses, nodal points of the Moon or the planets or other aspects with a negative influence; they are not elaborated in the calendar. If one has to sow at unfavourable times for practical reasons, one can choose favourable days for hoeing, which will improve the plant.

The position of the planets in the zodiac is shown in the box below, with the date of entry into a new constellation. R indicates the planet is moving retrograde (with the date when retrograde begins), D indicates the date when it moves in direct. motion again.

On the opposite calendar page astronomical aspects are indicated. Those visible to the naked eye are shown in **bold** type. Visible conjunctions (particularly Mercury's) are not always visible from all parts of the Earth.

Astronomical symbols

Constellations		*Planets*		*Aspects*			
♓	Pisces	☉	Sun	☊	Ascending node	**St**	Storms likely
♈	Aries	☾, ☽	Moon	☋	Descending node	⚡	Thunder likely
♉	Taurus	☿	Mercury	⌒	Highest Moon	**Eq**	Earthquakes
♊	Gemini	♀	Venus	⌣	Lowest Moon	**Tr**	Traffic dangers
♋	Cancer	♂	Mars	**Pg**	Perigee	**Vo**	Volcanic activity
♌	Leo	♃	Jupiter	**Ag**	Apogee		
♍	Virgo	♄	Saturn	☍	Opposition	■	Northern Trans-
♎	Libra	♅	Uranus	☌	Conjunction		planting Time
♏	Scorpio	♆	Neptune	☄	Eclipse/occultation		
♐	Sagittarius	♇	Pluto	☄	Lunar eclipse	■	Southern Trans-
♑	Capricorn	○	Full Moon	△	Trine (or ▲)		planting Time
♒	Aquarius	●	New Moon	E Earth	L Light/Air	W Water	H Warmth/Heat

Transplanting times

From midwinter through to midsummer the Sun rises earlier and sets later each day while its path across the sky ascends higher and higher. From midsummer until midwinter this is reversed, the days get shorter and the midday Sun shines from an ever lower point in the sky. This annual ascending and descending of the Sun creates our seasons. As it ascends and descends during the course of the year the Sun is slowly moving (from an Earth-centred point of view) through each of the twelve constellations of the zodiac in turn. On average it shines for one month from each constellation.

In the northern hemisphere the winter solstice occurs when the Sun is in the constellation of Sagittarius and the sum-mer solstice when it is in Gemini. At any point from Sagittarius to Gemini the Sun is ascending, while from Gemini to Sagittarius it is descending. In the southern hemisphere this is reversed.

The Moon (and all the planets) follow approximately the same path as the Sun around the zodiac but instead of a year, the Moon takes only about 27½ days to complete one cycle, shining from each constellation in turn for a period of two to three days. This means that the Moon will ascend for about fourteen days and then descend.

It is important to distinguish the journey of the Moon through the zodiac (siderial rhythm) from the waxing and waning (synodic) cycle: in any given constellation

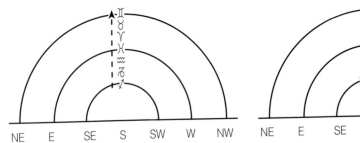
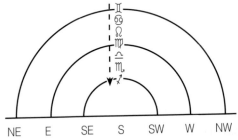

Northern hemisphere ascending Moon (left) and descending Moon (right): Transplanting Time

there may be a waxing, waning, full, quarter, sickle or gibbous Moon. As it moves through the zodiac the Moon, like the Sun, is ascending (in the northern hemisphere) when it is in the constellations from Sagittarius to Gemini and descending from Gemini to Sagittarius. In the southern hemisphere it is ascending from Gemini to Sagittarius and descending from Sagittarius to Gemini.

When the Moon is ascending, plant sap rises more strongly. The upper part of the plant fills with sap and vitality. This is a good time for cutting scions (for grafting). Fruit harvested during this period remains fresh for longer when stored.

When the Moon is descending, plants take root readily and connect well with their new location. This period is referred to as the **Transplanting Time.** Moving plants from one location to another is called *transplanting*. This is the case when young plants are moved from the seed bed into their final growing position but also when the gardener wishes to strengthen the root development of young fruit trees, shrubs or pot plants by frequently re-potting them. Sap movement is slower during the descending Moon. This is why it is a good time for trimming hedges, pruning trees and felling timber as well as applying compost to meadows, pastures and orchards.

Note that sowing is the moment when a seed is put into the soil; either the ascending or descending period can be used. It then needs time to germinate and grow. This is different from *transplanting* which is best done during the descending Moon. These times given in the calendar. Northern Transplanting Times refer to the northern hemisphere, and **Southern Transplanting Times** refer to the southern hemisphere. All other constellations and planetary aspects are equally valid in both hemispheres.

Local times

Times given are *Greenwich Mean Time* (GMT), using 24-hour clock with ^{h} after the time. Thus 15^h is 3 pm. **No account is taken of daylight saving (summer) time (DST).** Note 0^h is midnight at the beginning of a date, and 24^h is midnight at the end of the date.

Adjust as follows for different countries:

Europe

Britain, Ireland, Portugal, Iceland: GMT
(DST from March 30 to Oct 25, add 1^h)
Central Europe: add 1^h
(DST from March 30 to Oct 25, add 2^h)
Eastern Europe (Finland, etc.): add 2^h
(DST from March 30 to Oct 25, add 3^h)
Russia (Moscow), Georgia: add 4^h (no DST)

Africa/Asia

Namibia: add 1^h
(DST to April 5 & from Sep 7, add 2^h)
South Africa, Egypt: add 2^h (no DST)
Kenya: add 3^h (no DST)
Israel: add 2^h
(DST from March 28 to Oct 25, add 3^h)
Pakistan: add 5^h (no DST)
India: add $5\frac{1}{2}^h$ (no DST)
Bangladesh: add 6^h (no DST)
Philippines, China: add 8^h (no DST)
Japan: add 9^h (no DST)

Australia/New Zealand

Western Australia: add 8^h (no DST)
South Australia: add $9\frac{1}{2}^h$ (DST to April 5 & from Oct 5, add $10\frac{1}{2}^h$)
Northern Territory: add $9\frac{1}{2}^h$ (no DST)
Queensland: add 10^h (no DST)
ACT, NSW, Victoria, Tasmania: add 10^h
(DST to April 5 & from Oct 5, add 11^h)
New Zealand: add 12^h (DST to April 5 and from Sep 28, add 13^h)

North America

Newfoundland Standard Time: subtract $3\frac{1}{2}^h$
(DST March 9 to Nov 1, subtract $2\frac{1}{2}^h$)
Atlantic Standard Time: subtract 4^h
(DST March 9 to Nov 1, subtract 3^h)
Eastern Standard Time: subtract 5^h
(DST, March 9 to Nov 1, subtract 4^h)
Central Standard Time: subtract 6^h
(DST, except Saskatchewan March 9 to Nov 1, subtract 5^h)
Mountain Standard Time: subtract 7^h
(DST, except AZ, March 9 to Nov 1, subtract 6^h)
Pacific Standard Time: subtract 8^h
(DST March 9 to Nov 1, subtract 7^h)
Alaska Standard Time: subtract 9^h
(DST March 9 to Nov 1, subtract 8^h)
Hawaii Standard Time: subtract 10^h (no DST)
Mexico (mostly CST): subtract 6^h
(DST, April 6 to Oct 25, subtract 5^h)

South America

Argentina: subtract 3^h (no DST)
Brazil (Eastern): subtract 3^h (DST to Feb 15 and from Oct 19, subtract 2^h)
Chile: subtract 4^h (DST to March 8 and from Oct 12, subtract 3^h)
Columbia, Peru: subtract 5^h (no DST)

January 2014

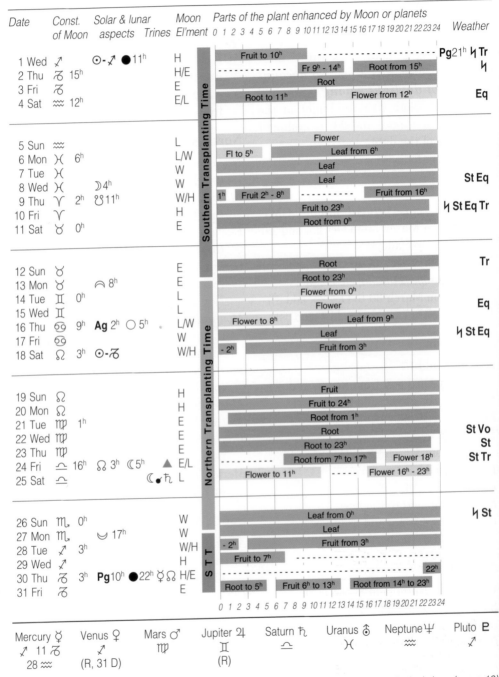

Date	Const. of Moon	Solar & lunar aspects	Moon Trines El'ment	Parts of the plant enhanced by Moon or planets	Weather
1 Wed	♐	☉-♐ ●11ʰ	H	Fruit to 10ʰ — Pg21ʰ	Pg21ʰ ♄ Tr / ♄
2 Thu	♑ 15ʰ		H/E	Fr 9ʰ - 14ʰ / Root from 15ʰ	
3 Fri	♑		E	Root	
4 Sat	♒ 12ʰ		E/L	Root to 11ʰ / Flower from 12ʰ	Eq
5 Sun	♒		L	Flower	
6 Mon	♓ 6ʰ		L/W	Fl to 5ʰ / Leaf from 6ʰ	
7 Tue	♓		W	Leaf	
8 Wed	♓	☽4ʰ	W	Leaf	St Eq
9 Thu	♈ 2ʰ	☊11ʰ	W/H	1ʰ Fruit 2ʰ - 8ʰ / Fruit from 16ʰ	♄ St Eq Tr
10 Fri	♈		H	Fruit to 23ʰ	
11 Sat	♉ 0ʰ		E	Root from 0ʰ	
12 Sun	♉		E	Root	Tr
13 Mon	♉	⌂ 8ʰ	E	Root to 23ʰ	
14 Tue	♊ 0ʰ		L	Flower from 0ʰ	Eq
15 Wed	♊		L	Flower	
16 Thu	♋ 9ʰ	Ag 2ʰ ○ 5ʰ	L/W	Flower to 8ʰ / Leaf from 9ʰ	♄ St Eq
17 Fri	♋		W	Leaf	
18 Sat	♌ 3ʰ	☉-♑	W/H	- 2ʰ / Fruit from 3ʰ	
19 Sun	♌		H	Fruit	
20 Mon	♌		H	Fruit to 24ʰ	
21 Tue	♍ 1ʰ		E	Root from 1ʰ	St Vo
22 Wed	♍		E	Root	St
23 Thu	♍		E	Root to 23ʰ	St Tr
24 Fri	♎ 16ʰ	☊ 3ʰ ☾5ʰ ▲	E/L	Root from 7ʰ to 17ʰ / Flower 18ʰ	
25 Sat	♎	☾•♄	L	Flower to 11ʰ / Flower 16ʰ - 23ʰ	
26 Sun	♏ 0ʰ		W	Leaf from 0ʰ	♄ St
27 Mon	♏	☋ 17ʰ	W	Leaf	
28 Tue	♐ 3ʰ		W/H	- 2ʰ / Fruit from 3ʰ	
29 Wed	♐		H	Fruit to 7ʰ	
30 Thu	♑ 3ʰ	Pg10ʰ ●22ʰ ☿☊	H/E	22ʰ	
31 Fri	♑		E	Root to 5ʰ / Fruit 6ʰ - 13ʰ / Root from 14ʰ to 23ʰ	

Southern Transplanting Time · *Northern Transplanting Time* · *STT*

Mercury ☿	Venus ♀	Mars ♂	Jupiter ♃	Saturn ♄	Uranus ♅	Neptune ♆	Pluto ♇
♐ 11 ♑	♐	♍	♊	♎	♓	♒	♐
28 ♒	(R, 31 D)		(R)				

NB: All zodiac symbols refer to astronomical constellations, not astrological signs (see p.10)

Planetary aspects
(Bold = visible to naked eye)

January 2014

1	☽☌♇ 12ʰ ☽☌☿ 15ʰ ☉☌♇ 19ʰ ☽☍♃ 19ʰ
2	☽☌♀ 11ʰ
3	☿☍♃ 7ʰ
4	☽☌♆ 22ʰ
5	☉☍♃ 21ʰ
6	
7	☽☌☊ 11ʰ ☽☍♂ 22ʰ ☿☌♀ 22ʰ
8	
9	
10	☽☍♄ 19ʰ
11	☉☌♀ 12ʰ
12	
13	
14	
15	☽☍♇ 0ʰ ☽☌♃ 5ʰ ☽☍♀ 14ʰ
16	
17	☾☍☿ 7ʰ
18	
19	☾☍♆ 9ʰ
20	
21	
22	☾☍☊ 6ʰ
23	☾☌♂ 4ʰ
24	☿△♂ 15ʰ
25	☾•♄ 14ʰ
26	
27	
28	
29	☾☌♇ 1ʰ ☾☌♃ 1ʰ ☾☌♀ 3ʰ
30	☿☌☊ 8ʰ
31	♃☍♇ 10ʰ

The Sun is in Sagittarius but on Jan 18 moves into Capricorn which could herald a cold period. Mars in Virgo throughout the month will emphasize the cold influence of Capricorn.

Until Jan 10 Mercury, and throughout the month Venus, moving retrorade, dominate Sagittarius. Pluto, moving very slowly, remains in Sagittarius throughout the year, and may bring some warmth. Jupiter moving retrograde in Gemini, Saturn in Libra, and Neptune in Aquarius provide Light influences. Only Uranus in Pisces mediates precipitation.

Northern Transplanting Time
Jan 13 11ʰ to Jan 27 14ʰ
Southern Transplanting Time
Dec 31 to Jan 13 7ʰ and Jan 27 18ʰ to Feb 9

The transplanting time is a good time for **pruning fruit trees, vines and hedges.** Fruit and Flower times are preferred for this work. Avoid unfavourable times (- - -).

Southern hemisphere harvest time for seeds
Fruit seeds: Fruit times after Jan 18.
Flower seeds: Flower times.
Leaf seeds: Leaf times up to Jan 18.
Root seeds: Root times; Jan 24 7ʰ to 17ʰ is especially good.

When **milk processing** it is best to avoid unfavourable times (- - -). This applies to both butter and cheese making. Milk which has been produced at Warmth/Fruit times yields the highest butterfat content. This is also the case on days with a tendency for thunderstorms. Times of moon perigee (**Pg**) are almost always unfavourable for milk processing and even yoghurt will not turn out well. Starter cultures from such days decay rapidly and it is advisable to produce double the amount the day before. Milk loves Light and Warmth times best of all. Water times are unsuitable.

Planet (naked eye) visibility
Evening: Mercury (from 19th), Venus (to 7th)
All night: Jupiter
Morning: Venus (from 14th), Mars, Saturn

February 2014

Date	Const. of Moon	Solar & lunar aspects	Moon Trines	El'ment	Parts of the plant enhanced by Moon or planets 0 1 2 3 4 5 6 7 8 9 10 11 12 13 14 15 16 17 18 19 20 21 22 23 24	Weather
1 Sat	♒ 0ʰ	☉-♑		L	Flower from 0ʰ	**Vo**
2 Sun	♓ 15ʰ			L/W	Flower to 14ʰ — Leaf from 15ʰ	
3 Mon	♓			W	Leaf	
4 Tue	♓			W	Leaf	
5 Wed	♈ 10ʰ	☊13ʰ		W/H	Leaf to 9ʰ — - - - - - - - - Fruit from 16ʰ	**St Vo**
6 Thu	♈	☽19ʰ		H	Fruit	
7 Fri	♉ 7ʰ			H/E	Fruit to 6ʰ — Root from 7ʰ	
8 Sat	♉			E	Root	
9 Sun	♉	⌒ 15ʰ		E	Root	**St**
10 Mon	♊ 6ʰ			E/L	Root to 5ʰ — Flower from 6ʰ	
11 Tue	♊			L	Flower	
12 Wed	♋ 15ʰ	**Ag** 5ʰ		L/W	Flower to 14ʰ — Leaf from 15ʰ	♄
13 Thu	♋			W	Leaf	
14 Fri	♌ 9ʰ	○ 24ʰ		W/H	Leaf to 8ʰ — Fruit from 9ʰ	**St Vo**
15 Sat	♌	☉-♒		H	Fruit to 22ʰ — 23	
16 Sun	♌		▲	H	Root to 14ʰ — Fruit from 15ʰ	♄ **St**
17 Mon	♍ 7ʰ			H/E	Fruit to 6ʰ — Root from 7ʰ	
18 Tue	♍			E	Root	
19 Wed	♍			E	Root to 23ʰ	
20 Thu	♎ 22ʰ	☊3ʰ		E/L	- - - - Root from 7ʰ to 21ʰ — 22ʰ - - - -	**Eq**
21 Fri	♎	☾•♄		L	Flower to 20ʰ	
22 Sat	♏ 7ʰ	☾ 17ʰ		L/W	Fl 1ʰ - 6ʰ — Leaf from 7ʰ	
23 Sun	♏			W	Leaf	♄
24 Mon	♐ 12ʰ	☋ 1ʰ		W/H	Leaf to 11ʰ — Fruit from 12ʰ	**St Vo**
25 Tue	♐			H	Fruit	
26 Wed	♑ 13ʰ	☾•♀		H/E	Fr -3ʰ - - - - - Fr 8ʰ-12ʰ — Root from 13ʰ	
27 Thu	♑	**Pg** 20ʰ		E	Root to 8ʰ — - - - - - - - - - - - -	
28 Fri	♒ 10ʰ			E/L	- - - - - - - - - Flower from 10ʰ	

Northern Transplanting Time
S T T

0 1 2 3 4 5 6 7 8 9 10 11 12 13 14 15 16 17 18 19 20 21 22 23 24

Mercury ☿ ♒ 16 ♑ (6 R, 28 D)	Venus ♀ ♐	Mars ♂ ♍	Jupiter ♃ ♊ (R)	Saturn ♄ ♎	Uranus ♅ ♓	Neptune ♆ ♒	Pluto ♇ ♐

NB: All zodiac symbols refer to astronomical constellations, not astrological signs (see p.10)

Planetary aspects
(Bold = visible to naked eye)

1 ☽☌☿ 5ʰ ☽☌♆ 11ʰ
2
3 ☽☌☊ 21ʰ
4 ☽☍♂ 23ʰ
5
6
7 ☽☍♄ 5ʰ
8

9
10
11 **☽☌♃ 5ʰ** ☽☍♇ 8ʰ ☽☍♀ 14ʰ
12
13
14
15 ☉△♂ 2ʰ ☾☍☿ 3ʰ ☾☍♆ 17ʰ ☉☌☿ 20ʰ

16 ☿△♂ 8ʰ
17
18 ☾☍☊ 14ʰ
19 **☾☌♂ 22ʰ**
20
21 **☾•♄ 22ʰ**
22

23 ☉☌♆ 18ʰ
24
25 ☾☍♃ 7ʰ ☾☌♇ 11ʰ
26 **☾•♀ 5ʰ**
27 ☾☌☿ 20ʰ ☾☌♆ 23ʰ
28

February 2014

The Sun moves from Capricorn to Aquarius on Feb 15, bringing Light influences. Mercury, moving retrograde from Feb 6 to 27, begins the month in Aquarius, and moves back into Capricorn on Feb 16. Venus remains in the Warmth constellation of Sagittarius throughout the month. Mars, though, brings cold from Virgo.

Jupiter moving retrograde in Gemini, Saturn in Libra, and Neptune in Aquarius provide Light influences. Pluto, as in January, remains in Sagittarius. Only Uranus in Pisces is able to mediate Water influences and bring rain showers.

Northern Transplanting Time
Feb 9 17ʰ to Feb 23 24ʰ
Southern Transplanting Time
Jan 27 to Feb 9 14ʰ and Feb 24 4ʰ to March 8

Vines, fruit trees and shrubs can be pruned during the transplanting period selecting Flower and Fruit times in preference. Unfavourable times (- - -) should be avoided.

Southern hemisphere harvest time for seeds
Fruit seeds: Any Fruit times during this month.
Flower seeds: Flower times from Feb 20.

Best times for taking **willow cuttings for hedges and fences:** Feb 24 13ʰ to Feb 26 3ʰ, from Feb 28 10ʰ to March 2 1ʰ.

Planet (naked eye) visibility
Evening: Mercury (to 9th)
All night: Jupiter
Morning: Venus, Mars, Saturn

March 2014

All times in GMT

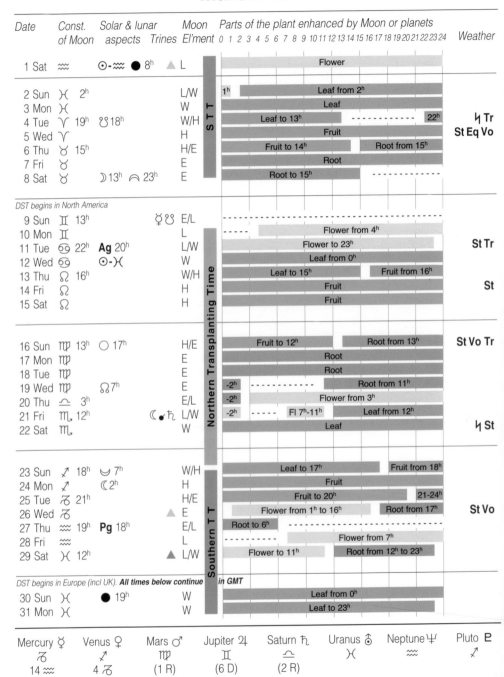

Date	Const. of Moon	Solar & lunar aspects	Trines	Moon El'ment	Parts of the plant enhanced by Moon or planets (0–24h)	Transplanting time	Weather
1 Sat	♒	☉-♒ ● 8^h	▲	L	Flower	S T T	
2 Sun	♓ 2^h			L/W	1^h / Leaf from 2^h	S T T	
3 Mon	♓			W	Leaf	S T T	
4 Tue	♈ 19^h	☋18^h		W/H	Leaf to 13^h - - - - - - 22^h	S T T	ɥ Tr
5 Wed	♈			H	Fruit	S T T	St Eq Vo
6 Thu	♉ 15^h			H/E	Fruit to 14^h / Root from 15^h	S T T	
7 Fri	♉			E	Root	S T T	
8 Sat	♉	☽13^h ⋒ 23^h		E	Root to 15^h - - - - - -	S T T	
DST begins in North America							
9 Sun	♊ 13^h		☿☋	E/L	- - - - - - - - - - - -		
10 Mon	♊			L	- - - - Flower from 4^h	Northern Transplanting Time	
11 Tue	♋ 22^h	**Ag** 20^h		L/W	Flower to 23^h	Northern Transplanting Time	St Tr
12 Wed	♋	☉-♓		W	Leaf from 0^h	Northern Transplanting Time	
13 Thu	♌ 16^h			W/H	Leaf to 15^h / Fruit from 16^h	Northern Transplanting Time	
14 Fri	♌			H	Fruit	Northern Transplanting Time	St
15 Sat	♌			H	Fruit	Northern Transplanting Time	
16 Sun	♍ 13^h	○ 17^h		H/E	Fruit to 12^h / Root from 13^h	Northern Transplanting Time	St Vo Tr
17 Mon	♍			E	Root	Northern Transplanting Time	
18 Tue	♍			E	Root	Northern Transplanting Time	
19 Wed	♍	☊7^h		E	-2^h - - - - - - Root from 11^h	Northern Transplanting Time	
20 Thu	♎ 3^h			E/L	-2^h / Flower from 3^h	Northern Transplanting Time	
21 Fri	♏ 12^h		☾☌♄	L/W	-2^h - - - - Fl 7^h-11^h / Leaf from 12^h	Northern Transplanting Time	
22 Sat	♏			W	Leaf	Northern Transplanting Time	ɥ St
23 Sun	♐ 18^h	⋓ 7^h		W/H	Leaf to 17^h / Fruit from 18^h	Southern T T	
24 Mon	♐	☾2^h		H	Fruit	Southern T T	
25 Tue	♑ 21^h			H/E	Fruit to 20^h / 21-24^h	Southern T T	
26 Wed	♑		▲	E	Flower from 1^h to 16^h / Root from 17^h	Southern T T	St Vo
27 Thu	♒ 19^h	**Pg** 18^h		E/L	Root to 6^h - - - - - - - -	Southern T T	
28 Fri	♒			L	- - - - - Flower from 7^h	Southern T T	
29 Sat	♓ 12^h		▲	L/W	Flower to 11^h / Root from 12^h to 23^h	Southern T T	
DST begins in Europe (incl UK). ***All times below continue in GMT***							
30 Sun	♓	● 19^h		W	Leaf from 0^h	Southern T T	
31 Mon	♓			W	Leaf to 23^h	Southern T T	

Mercury ☿	Venus ♀	Mars ♂	Jupiter ♃	Saturn ♄	Uranus ♅	Neptune ♆	Pluto ♇
♑	♐	♍	♊	♎	♓	♒	♐
14 ♒	4 ♑	(1 R)	(6 D)	(2 R)			

NB: All zodiac symbols refer to astronomical constellations, not astrological signs *(see p. 10)*

Planetary aspects
(Bold = visible to naked eye)

March

1 $\odot\triangle\jupiter$ 4^h

2

3 $\moon\conjunction\ascnode$ 10^h

4 $\moon\opposition\mars$ 15^h

5

6 $\moon\opposition\saturn$ 14^h

7

8

9 $\mercury\descnode$ 15^h

10 $\moon\conjunction\jupiter$ 11^h $\moon\opposition\pluto$ 16^h

11

12 $\moon\opposition\venus$ 14^h

13 $\odot\triangle\saturn$ 21^h

14 $\moon\opposition\mercury$ 6^h $\mercury\triangle\mars$ 16^h

15 $\moon\opposition\neptune$ 2^h

16

17 $\moon\opposition\ascnode$ 23^h

18

19 $\moon\conjunction\mars$ 1^h

20

21 $\moon\bullet\saturn$ 3^h

22 $\mercury\conjunction\neptune$ 20^h

23

24 $\moon\opposition\jupiter$ 15^h $\moon\conjunction\pluto$ 19^h

25

26 $\mercury\triangle\jupiter$ 13^h

27 $\moon\conjunction\venus$ 8^h

28 $\moon\conjunction\neptune$ 10^h

29 $\moon\conjunction\mercury$ 0^h $\venus\triangle\mars$ 19^h

30 $\moon\conjunction\ascnode$ 23^h

31 $\moon\opposition\mars$ 15^h

Planet (naked eye) visibility
Evening: Jupiter
All night: Mars
Morning: Venus, Saturn

On March 12 the Sun moves from Aquarius into Pisces. Together with Uranus in Pisces this could bring about precipitation. Mercury in Capricorn moves into Aquarius on March 14. Together with Jupiter in Gemini, Saturn in Libra and Neptune in Aquarius, this brings Light influences.

Venus moves from Sagittarius to Capricorn on March 4, contributing to the cold influence of Mars, now retrograde, in Virgo.

Pluto in Sagittarius is the only planet in a Warmth constellation.

Northern Transplanting Time
March 10 4^h to March 23 5^h
Southern Transplanting Time
Feb 24 to March 8 13^h and March 23 11^h to April 5

Willow cuttings for **pollen production** are best cut from March 10 4^h to March 11 23^h; and for **honey flow** from March 13 16^h to March 16 12^h.

The cuttings taken in February are best stuck in the ground during transplanting time; to improve pollen production do this at Flower times, and to increase honey flow do this at Fruit times.

Control slugs from March 12 0^h to March 13 15^h.

Cuttings for grafting: Feb 28 10^h to March 8 15^h, and March 10 4^h to March 11 23^h, always choosing times (Fruit, Leaf, etc.) according to part of plant to be enhanced.

April 2014

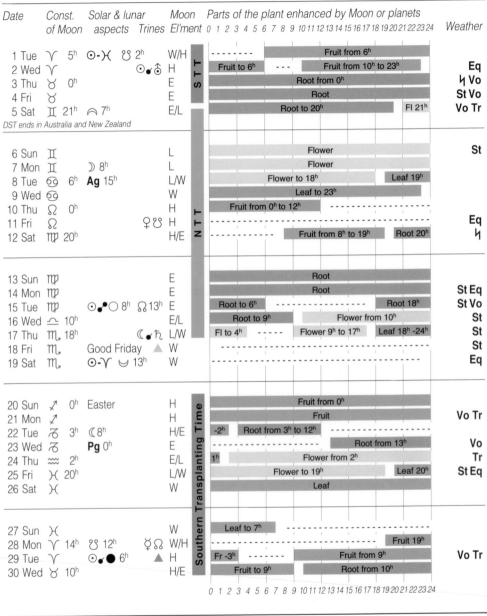

Date	Const. of Moon	Solar & lunar aspects	Trines	Moon El'ment	Parts of the plant enhanced by Moon or planets	Weather
1 Tue	♈ 5ʰ	☉-♓ ☋ 2ʰ		W/H	Fruit from 6ʰ	
2 Wed	♈	☉•♁		H	Fruit to 6ʰ --- Fruit from 10ʰ to 23ʰ	Eq
3 Thu	♉ 0ʰ			E	Root from 0ʰ	♄ Vo
4 Fri	♉			E	Root	St Vo
5 Sat	♊ 21ʰ	⋒ 7ʰ		E/L	Root to 20ʰ Fl 21ʰ	Vo Tr

DST ends in Australia and New Zealand

6 Sun	♊			L	Flower	St
7 Mon	♊	☽ 8ʰ		L	Flower	
8 Tue	♋ 6ʰ	**Ag** 15ʰ		L/W	Flower to 18ʰ Leaf 19ʰ	
9 Wed	♋			W	Leaf to 23ʰ	
10 Thu	♌ 0ʰ			H	Fruit from 0ʰ to 12ʰ	
11 Fri	♌	♀ ☋		H	Fruit from 8ʰ to 19ʰ Root 20ʰ	Eq
12 Sat	♍ 20ʰ			H/E	Fruit from 8ʰ to 19ʰ Root 20ʰ	♄

13 Sun	♍			E	Root	
14 Mon	♍			E	Root	St Eq
15 Tue	♍	☉•♂○ 8ʰ ☊13ʰ		E	Root to 6ʰ Root 18ʰ	St Vo
16 Wed	♎ 10ʰ			E/L	Root to 9ʰ Flower from 10ʰ	St
17 Thu	♏ 18ʰ	☾•♄		L/W	Fl to 4ʰ ----- Flower 9ʰ to 17ʰ Leaf 18ʰ -24ʰ	St
18 Fri	♏	Good Friday ▲		W		St
19 Sat	♏	☉-♈ ⋓ 13ʰ		W		Eq

20 Sun	♐ 0ʰ	Easter		H	Fruit from 0ʰ	
21 Mon	♐			H	Fruit	Vo Tr
22 Tue	♑ 3ʰ	☾ 8ʰ		H/E	-2ʰ Root from 3ʰ to 12ʰ	
23 Wed	♑	**Pg** 0ʰ		E	Root from 13ʰ	Vo
24 Thu	♒ 2ʰ			E/L	1ʰ Flower from 2ʰ	Tr
25 Fri	♓ 20ʰ			L/W	Flower to 19ʰ Leaf 20ʰ	St Eq
26 Sat	♓			W	Leaf	

27 Sun	♓			W	Leaf to 7ʰ	
28 Mon	♈ 14ʰ	☋ 12ʰ	☿ ☊	W/H	Fruit 19ʰ	
29 Tue	♈	☉•● 6ʰ ▲		H	Fr -3ʰ Fruit from 9ʰ	Vo Tr
30 Wed	♉ 10ʰ			H/E	Fruit to 9ʰ Root from 10ʰ	

Left margin labels: STT, NTT, Southern Transplanting Time

0 1 2 3 4 5 6 7 8 9 10 11 12 13 14 15 16 17 18 19 20 21 22 23 24

Mercury ☿	Venus ♀	Mars ♂	Jupiter ♃	Saturn ♄	Uranus ♅	Neptune ♆	Pluto ♇
♒ 2 ♓	♑ 2 ♒	♍	♊	♎	♓	♒	♐
23 ♈	25 ♓	(R)		(R)			(14 R)

NB: All zodiac symbols refer to astronomical constellations, not astrological signs (see p.10)

Planetary aspects
(Bold = *visible to naked eye)*

1
2 ☉●⛢ 7^h ☽☍♄ 22^h
3 ☿△♄ 3^h
4
5

6 **☽☌♃ 22^h**
7 ☽☍♇ 1^h
8 ☉☍♂ 21^h
9
10
11 ☽☍♀ 10^h ☽☍♆ 11^h ♀☋ 19^h
12 ♀☌♆ 3^h

13
14 ☽☍☿ 7^h ☽☍⛢ 9^h **☽☌♂ 16^h** ☿☌⛢ 23^h
15
16 ☿☍♂ 11^h
17 **☾●♄ 7^h**
18 ♀△♃ 1^h
19

20 ♃☍♇ 23^h
21 ☾☌♇ 1^h ☾☍♃ 1^h
22
23 ♂☍⛢ 7^h
24 ☾☌♆ 19^h
25 ♀△♄ 5^h **☾☌♀ 20^h**
26 ☉☌☿ 4^h

27 ☾☍♂ 7^h ☾☌⛢ 10^h
28 ☿☊ 7^h
29 ☽☌☿ 14^h ☿△♇ 18^h
30 ☽☍♄ 4^h

Planet (naked eye) visibility
Evening: Jupiter
All night: Mars, Saturn
Morning: Venus

April 2014

Pisces harbours the Sun until April 18, Mercury from April 2 to 22 and Uranus all month. This could bring rain. In the second part of the month, the Sun (from April 19) and Mercury (from April 23) move into Aries, and the Warmth influence is supported by Pluto (retrograde from April 14) in Sagittarius.

Jupiter in Gemini and Venus (from April 2 to 24) in Aquarius are supported strongly by Saturn retrograde in Libra in bringing Light influences. Mars in Virgo is retrograde, thus bringing influences of cold particularly strongly.

There may be warm and sunny spring days, but also showers, much needed at this time of year.

Northern Transplanting Time
April 5 10^h to April 17 24^h
Southern Transplanting Time
March 23 to April 5 6^h
and April 20 0^h to May 2

Grafting of fruiting shrubs from April 20 0^h to April 22 2^h and April 28 19^h to April 30 9^h, avoiding brief unfavourable time (**- - -**).

Grafting of flowering shrubs from April 24 2^h to April 25 19^h.

Control slugs on April 8 6^h to April 9 23^h.

Southern hemisphere harvest time for seeds
Choose Fruit, Flower, Leaf, Root times according to type of plant, and avoid unfavourable times (**- - -**).

May 2014

All times in GMT

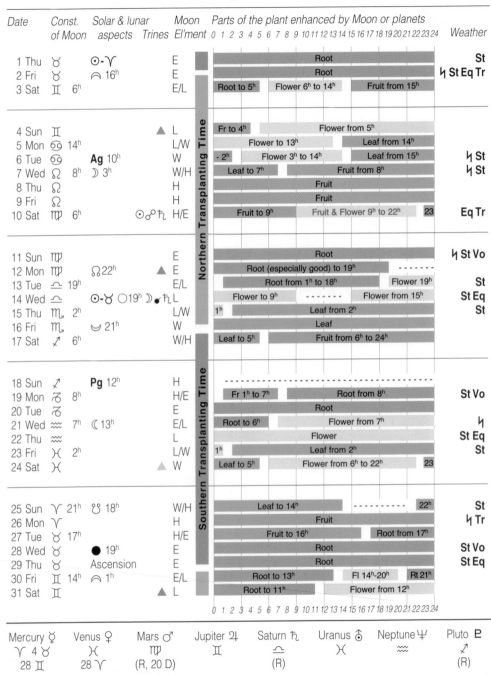

Date	Const. of Moon	Solar & lunar aspects	Trines	Moon El'ment	Parts of the plant enhanced by Moon or planets	Weather
1 Thu	♉	☉-♈		E	Root	St
2 Fri	♉	⌢ 16ʰ		E	Root	♄ St Eq Tr
3 Sat	♊ 6ʰ			E/L	Root to 5ʰ · Flower 6ʰ to 14ʰ · Fruit from 15ʰ	
4 Sun	♊		▲	L	Fr to 4ʰ · Flower from 5ʰ	
5 Mon	♋ 14ʰ			L/W	Flower to 13ʰ · Leaf from 14ʰ	
6 Tue	♋	Ag 10ʰ		W	- 2ʰ · Flower 3ʰ to 14ʰ · Leaf from 15ʰ	♄ St
7 Wed	♌ 8ʰ	☽ 3ʰ		W/H	Leaf to 7ʰ · Fruit from 8ʰ	♄ St
8 Thu	♌			H	Fruit	
9 Fri	♌			H	Fruit	
10 Sat	♍ 6ʰ	☉♂♄		H/E	Fruit to 9ʰ · Fruit & Flower 9ʰ to 22ʰ · 23	Eq Tr
11 Sun	♍			E	Root	♄ St Vo
12 Mon	♍	♌22ʰ	▲	E	Root (especially good) to 19ʰ	
13 Tue	⌢ 19ʰ			E/L	Root from 1ʰ to 18ʰ · Flower 19ʰ	St
14 Wed	⌢	☉-♉ ○19ʰ ☽♄		L	Flower to 9ʰ · Flower from 15ʰ	St Eq
15 Thu	♏ 2ʰ			L/W	1ʰ · Leaf from 2ʰ	St
16 Fri	♏	⌣ 21ʰ		W	Leaf	
17 Sat	♐ 6ʰ			W/H	Leaf to 5ʰ · Fruit from 6ʰ to 24ʰ	
18 Sun	♐	Pg 12ʰ		H		St Vo
19 Mon	♑ 8ʰ			H/E	Fr 1ʰ to 7ʰ · Root from 8ʰ	
20 Tue	♑			E	Root	
21 Wed	♒ 7ʰ	☾ 13ʰ		E/L	Root to 6ʰ · Flower from 7ʰ	♄
22 Thu	♒			L	Flower	St Eq
23 Fri	♓ 2ʰ			L/W	1ʰ · Leaf from 2ʰ	St
24 Sat	♓		▲	W	Leaf to 5ʰ · Flower from 6ʰ to 22ʰ · 23	
25 Sun	♈ 21ʰ	☍ 18ʰ		W/H	Leaf to 14ʰ · 22ʰ	St
26 Mon	♈			H	Fruit	♄ Tr
27 Tue	♉ 17ʰ			H/E	Fruit to 16ʰ · Root from 17ʰ	
28 Wed	♉	● 19ʰ		E	Root	St Vo
29 Thu	♉	Ascension		E	Root	St Eq
30 Fri	♊ 14ʰ	⌢ 1ʰ		E/L	Root to 13ʰ · Fl 14ʰ-20ʰ · Rt 21ʰ	
31 Sat	♊		▲	L	Root to 11ʰ · Flower from 12ʰ	

Northern Transplanting Time

Southern Transplanting Time

0 1 2 3 4 5 6 7 8 9 10 11 12 13 14 15 16 17 18 19 20 21 22 23 24

Mercury ☿	Venus ♀	Mars ♂	Jupiter ♃	Saturn ♄	Uranus ♅	Neptune ♆	Pluto ♇
♈ 4 ♉	♓	♍	♊	⌢	♓	♒	♐
28 ♊	28 ♈	(R, 20 D)		(R)			(R)

NB: All zodiac symbols refer to astronomical constellations, not astrological signs (see p.10)

Planetary aspects

(Bold = *visible to naked eye)*

1
2
3 ☿☍♄ 1^h
4 ☉△♇ 0^h ☽☍♇ 9^h **☽☌♃ 13^h**
5
6
7
8 ☽☍♆ 21^h
9
10 ☉☍♄ 18^h
11 ♀☍♂ 9^h **☽☌♂ 11^h** ☽☍♀ 12^h ☽☍♅ 21^h
12 **☿△♂ 16^h**
13
14 **☽•♄ 12^h**
15
16 ♀☌♅ 0^h ☾☍☿ 8^h
17
18 ☾☌♇ 6^h ☾☍♃ 14^h
19
20
21
22 ☾☌♆ 1^h
23
24 ☾☍♂ 8^h **♃△♄ 18^h** ☾☌♅ 19^h
25 **☾☌♀ 14^h**
26
27 ☾☍♄ 8^h
28
29
30 **☽☌☿ 16^h**
31 ☉△♂ 8^h ☽☍♇ 16^h

Planet (naked eye) visibility
Evening: Mercury (from 6th), Jupiter
All night: Mars, Saturn
Morning: Venus

May 2014

The Sun moves from Aries to cooler Taurus on May 14. Mercury, except for the first and last few days of the month, also brings its cool influence from Taurus. Mars, retrograde until May 20, emphasizes this from Virgo.

Venus remains in Pisces until May 28, supporting Uranus in the same constellation, and bringing rain.

Jupiter in Gemini, helped by Saturn (retrograde in Libra) and Neptune in Aquarius bring Light influences, including a Warmth trine on May 24. Only Pluto, retrograde in Sagittarius, brings Warmth influences.

The prospects for May are not too good. Let us hope the weather gods take some pity on the month of May!

Northern Transplanting Time
May 2 18^h to May 16 19^h and
May 30 4^h to June 13
Southern Transplanting Time
April 20 to May 2 13^h and
May 17 1^h to May 29 23^h

The **soil warms up** on May 4.

Plant **table potatoes** from May 10 23^h to May 13 18^h, May 27 17^h to May 30 13^h, and May 30 21^h to May 31 11^h. **Transplant seed potatoes** for 2015 from May 25 22^h to May 27 16^h.

Hay should be cut at Flower times.

Control:
Insect pests, Colorado beetle and varroa from May 27 17^h to May 30 13^h.
Flies by burning fly papers in the cow barn at Flower times.
Mole crickets from May 15 2^h to May 17 5^h.

Begin **queen bee** rearing at Flower times.

Biodynamic preparations should be dug out from May 3 22^h to May 5 13^h.

June 2014

All times in GMT

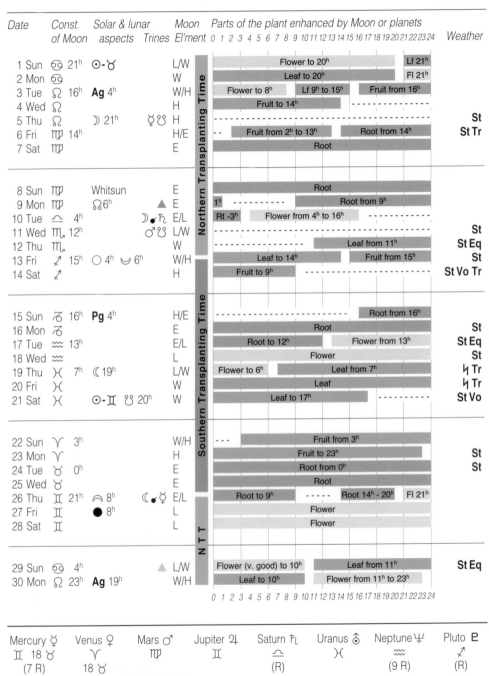

Date	Const. of Moon	Solar & lunar aspects	Trines	Moon El'ment	Parts of the plant enhanced by Moon or planets (0–24)	Weather
1 Sun	♋ 21ʰ	☉-♉		L/W	Flower to 20ʰ — Lf 21ʰ	
2 Mon	♋			W	Leaf to 20ʰ — Fl 21ʰ	
3 Tue	♌ 16ʰ	Ag 4ʰ		W/H	Flower to 8ʰ — Lf 9ʰ to 15ʰ — Fruit from 16ʰ	
4 Wed	♌			H	Fruit to 14ʰ	
5 Thu	♌	☽ 21ʰ	☿ ♉	H		St
6 Fri	♍ 14ʰ			H/E	Fruit from 2ʰ to 13ʰ — Root from 14ʰ	St Tr
7 Sat	♍			E	Root	
8 Sun	♍	Whitsun		E	Root	
9 Mon	♍	♌6ʰ	▲	E	1ʰ — Root from 9ʰ	
10 Tue	♎ 4ʰ		☽•♄	E/L	Rt -3ʰ — Flower from 4ʰ to 16ʰ	
11 Wed	♏ 12ʰ		♂ ♉	L/W		St
12 Thu	♏			W	Leaf from 11ʰ	St Eq
13 Fri	♐ 15ʰ	○ 4ʰ ♆ 6ʰ		W/H	Leaf to 14ʰ — Fruit from 15ʰ	St
14 Sat	♐			H	Fruit to 9ʰ	St Vo Tr
15 Sun	♑ 16ʰ	Pg 4ʰ		H/E	Root from 16ʰ	
16 Mon	♑			E	Root	St
17 Tue	♒ 13ʰ			E/L	Root to 12ʰ — Flower from 13ʰ	St Eq
18 Wed	♒			L	Flower	St
19 Thu	♓ 7ʰ	☾ 19ʰ		L/W	Flower to 6ʰ — Leaf from 7ʰ	♄ Tr
20 Fri	♓			W	Leaf	♄ Tr
21 Sat	♓	☉-♊ ♉ 20ʰ		W	Leaf to 17ʰ	St Vo
22 Sun	♈ 3ʰ			W/H	Fruit from 3ʰ	
23 Mon	♈			H	Fruit to 23ʰ	St
24 Tue	♉ 0ʰ			E	Root from 0ʰ	St
25 Wed	♉			E	Root	
26 Thu	♊ 21ʰ	♎ 8ʰ	☾•☿	E/L	Root to 9ʰ — Root 14ʰ - 20ʰ — Fl 21ʰ	
27 Fri	♊	● 8ʰ		L	Flower	
28 Sat	♊			L	Flower	
29 Sun	♋ 4ʰ		▲	L/W	Flower (v. good) to 10ʰ — Leaf from 11ʰ	St Eq
30 Mon	♌ 23ʰ	Ag 19ʰ		W/H	Leaf to 10ʰ — Flower from 11ʰ to 23ʰ	

Northern Transplanting Time: 1–14
Southern Transplanting Time: 15–28
N T T: 29–30

Mercury ☿	Venus ♀	Mars ♂	Jupiter ♃	Saturn ♄	Uranus ♅	Neptune ♆	Pluto ♇
♊ 18 ♉ (7 R)	♈ / 18 ♉	♍	♊	♎ (R)	♓	♒ (9 R)	♐ (R)

NB: All zodiac symbols refer to astronomical constellations, not astrological signs (see p.10)

Planetary aspects
(Bold = *visible to naked eye*)

June 2014

1 ☽☍♃ 7^h
2
3
4
5 ☽☍♆ 6^h ☿☊ 14^h
6
7

8 ☽☌♂ 0^h ☽☍♁ 8^h
9 ♀△♇ 2^h
10 ☽☍♀ 13^h ☽•♄ 19^h
11 ♂☊ 22^h
12
13 ♀☍♄ 4^h ☾☍☿ 20^h
14 ☾☌♇ 14^h

15 ☾☌♃ 7^h
16
17
18 ☾☌♆ 7^h
19 ☉☌☿ 23^h
20 ☾☍♂ 23^h
21 ☾☌♁ 2^h

22
23 ☾☍♄ 11^h
24 ☾☌♀ 13^h
25 ♂☍♁ 8^h
26 ☾•☿ 12^h
27 ☽☍♇ 22^h
28

29 ☽☍♃ 1^h ☉△♆ 7^h
30

The Sun moves from Taurus to Gemini on June 21. Mercury in Gemini becomes retrograde on June 7, moving back into Taurus on June 18. On that same day Venus also moves into Taurus, direct from Aries. This may bring cool weather, at least at night. Mars is in Virgo for the entire month, reinforcing the cool, Earth element.

Saturn in Libra is retrograde, thus making the Light influence particularly strong. This is supported by Jupiter in Gemini, and Neptune in Aquarius (also retrograde from June 9).

Uranus in Pisces is alone in caring for rainy influences. Pluto, retrograde, is in the Warmth constellation of Sagittarius throughout the month.

There may be sunny summer days with cool nights.

Northern Transplanting Time
May 30 to June 13 5^h and
June 26 11^h to July 10
Southern Transplanting Time
June 13 9^h to June 26 7^h

Cut **hay** at Flower times. June 30 11^h to 23^h is particularly good.

Begin **queen bee** rearing on June 10 4^h to 16^h, June 17 13^h to June 19 6^h or at other Flower times.

Control:
Flies by burning fly papers in the cow barn at Flower times.
Mole crickets ash from June 11 12^h to June 13 14^h.
Grasshoppers June 26 21^h to June 29 3^h.

Planet (naked eye) visibility
Evening: Mercury (to 2nd), Mars, Jupiter
All night: Saturn
Morning: Venus

July 2014

All times in GMT

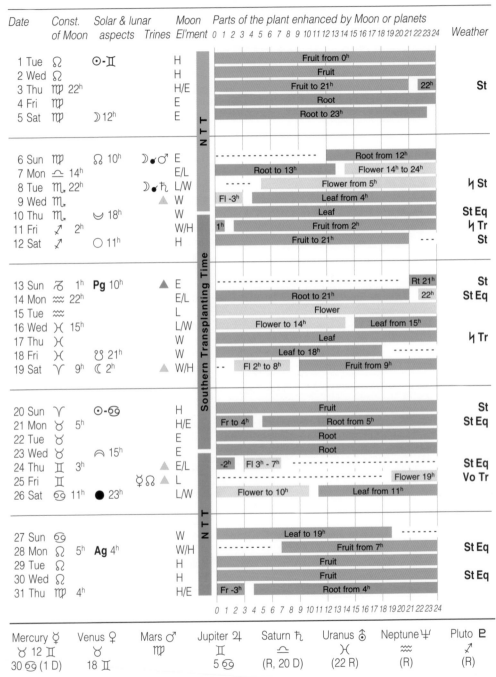

Date	Const. of Moon	Solar & lunar aspects	Trines	Moon El'ment	Parts of the plant enhanced by Moon or planets	Weather

NTT / Southern Transplanting Time / NTT

1 Tue ♌ ☉-♊ — H — Fruit from 0ʰ
2 Wed ♌ — H — Fruit
3 Thu ♍ 22ʰ — H/E — Fruit to 21ʰ 22ʰ — St
4 Fri ♍ — E — Root
5 Sat ♍ ☽12ʰ — E — Root to 23ʰ

6 Sun ♍ ♌ 10ʰ ☽☌♂ E — Root from 12ʰ
7 Mon ♎ 14ʰ — E/L — Root to 13ʰ / Flower 14ʰ to 24ʰ
8 Tue ♏ 22ʰ ☽☌♄ L/W — Flower from 5ʰ — ♄ St
9 Wed ♏ ▲ W — Fl -3ʰ / Leaf from 4ʰ
10 Thu ♏ � 18ʰ W — Leaf — St Eq
11 Fri ♐ 2ʰ — W/H — 1ʰ Fruit from 2ʰ — ♄ Tr
12 Sat ♐ ○ 11ʰ — H — Fruit to 21ʰ — St

13 Sun ♑ 1ʰ **Pg** 10ʰ ▲ E — Rt 21ʰ — St
14 Mon ♒ 22ʰ — E/L — Root to 21ʰ 22ʰ — St Eq
15 Tue ♒ — L — Flower
16 Wed ♓ 15ʰ — L/W — Flower to 14ʰ / Leaf from 15ʰ
17 Thu ♓ — W — Leaf — ♄ Tr
18 Fri ♓ ♅ 21ʰ — W — Leaf to 18ʰ
19 Sat ♈ 9ʰ ☽ 2ʰ ▲ W/H — Fl 2ʰ to 8ʰ / Fruit from 9ʰ

20 Sun ♈ ☉-♋ H — Fruit — St
21 Mon ♉ 5ʰ — H/E — Fr to 4ʰ / Root from 5ʰ — St Eq
22 Tue ♉ — E — Root
23 Wed ♉ ♁ 15ʰ E — Root
24 Thu ♊ 3ʰ ▲ E/L — -2ʰ Fl 3ʰ - 7ʰ — St Eq
25 Fri ♊ ☿♌ ▲ L — Flower 19ʰ — Vo Tr
26 Sat ♋ 11ʰ ● 23ʰ L/W — Flower to 10ʰ / Leaf from 11ʰ

27 Sun ♋ — W — Leaf to 19ʰ
28 Mon ♌ 5ʰ **Ag** 4ʰ W/H — Fruit from 7ʰ — St Eq
29 Tue ♌ — H — Fruit
30 Wed ♌ — H — Fruit — St Eq
31 Thu ♍ 4ʰ — H/E — Fr -3ʰ / Root from 4ʰ

Mercury ☿	Venus ♀	Mars ♂	Jupiter ♃	Saturn ♄	Uranus ♅	Neptune ♆	Pluto ♇
♉ 12 ♊	♉	♍	♊	♎	♓	♒	♐
30 ♋ (1 D)	18 ♊		5 ♋	(R, 20 D)	(22 R)	(R)	(R)

30   *NB: All zodiac symbols refer to astronomical constellations, not astrological signs (see p.10)*

Planetary aspects

(**Bold** = *visible to naked eye*)

1
2   ☽☍♆ 13^h
3
4   ☉☍♇ 8^h
5   ☽☍☋ 18^h

6   ☽•♂ 2^h
7
8   ☽•♄ 2^h
9   ☉△♄ 0^h
10   ☽☍♀ 12^h
11   ☽☍☿ 0^h ☾☌♇ 23^h
12

13   ☾☍♃ 2^h ♀△♂ 8^h
14
15   ☾☌♆ 14^h
16
17
18   ☾☌☋ 9^h
19   ☾☍♂ 2^h ☿△♆ 6^h

20   ☾☍♄ 15^h
21
22   ☿☍♇ 7^h
23
24   ♀△♆ 11^h ☾☌♀ 18^h ☉☌♃ 21^h
25   ☿△♄ 2^h ☾☍♇ 2^h ♀☊ 6^h ☾☌☿ 14^h
26   ☾☌♃ 20^h

27
28   ♀☍♇ 7^h
29   ☽☍♆ 18^h
30
31

Planet (naked eye) visibility
Evening: Mars, Jupiter (to 3rd)
All night: Saturn
Morning: Venus

July 2014

The Sun moving from Gemini into Cancer on July 20 could bring some warm rain showers.

Saturn in Libra (retrograde to July 20) and Neptune in Aquarius bring Light influences. Mercury, in Gemini from July 12 to 30, and Venus from July 18 add to this. The Light character of the month is further emphasized by four Light trines on July 9, 19, 24 and 25. However, Mercury's node on July 25 inhibits their full potential.

On July 5 Jupiter moves from Gemini into watery Cancer, serving as rain bringer together with Uranus in Pisces. Mars in Virgo remains in the cold Earth element. Only Pluto in Sagittarius mediates Warmth.

Northern Transplanting Time
June 26 to July 10 16^h and
July 23 18^h to Aug 7
Southern Transplanting Time
July 10 20^h to July 23 14^h

Late hay cut at Flower times.

Summer harvest for seeds:
Flower plants: Harvest at Flower times.
Similarly, harvest **fruit plants** at Fruit times, and **root plants** at Root times. **Leaf plants,** if really necessary, from July 26 11^h to July 27 19^h.

Control
Grasshoppers: from July 24 3^h to July 28 4^h.
Flies: burn fly papers in the cow barn at Flower times, avoiding unfavourable times (- - -).
Slugs: spray leaf plants and the soil with horn silica early in the morning during Leaf times. Burn from July 26 11^h to July 28 4^h.

July

August 2014

All times in GMT

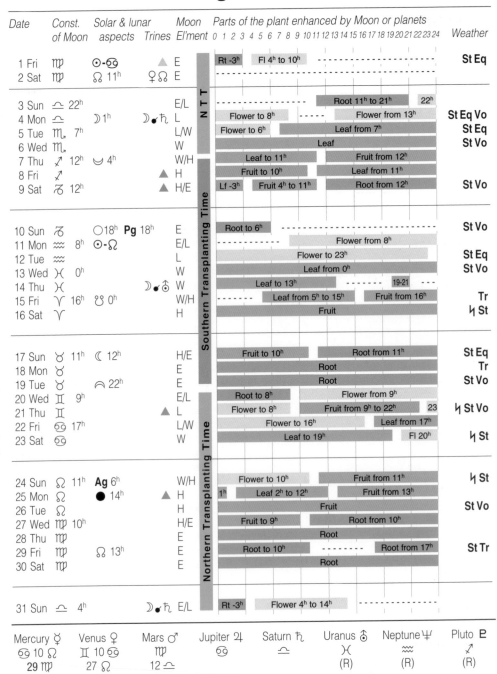

Date	Const. of Moon	Solar & lunar aspects	Trines	Moon El'ment		Parts of the plant enhanced by Moon or planets (0–24)	Weather
1 Fri	♍	☉-♋	▲	E	NTT	Rt -3^h; Fl 4^h to 10^h; - - - -	St Eq
2 Sat	♍	☊ 11^h	♀☊	E	NTT	- - - -	
3 Sun	♎ 22^h			E/L	NTT	- - - -; Root 11^h to 21^h; 22^h	
4 Mon	♎	☽ 1^h	☽☌♄	L	NTT	Flower to 8^h; - - - -; Flower from 13^h	St Eq Vo
5 Tue	♏ 7^h			L/W	NTT	Flower to 6^h; Leaf from 7^h	St Eq
6 Wed	♏			W	NTT	Leaf	St Vo
7 Thu	♐ 12^h	◡ 4^h		W/H	Southern Transplanting Time	Leaf to 11^h; Fruit from 12^h	
8 Fri	♐		▲	H	Southern Transplanting Time	Fruit to 10^h; Leaf from 11^h	
9 Sat	♑ 12^h		▲	H/E	Southern Transplanting Time	Lf -3^h; Fruit 4^h to 11^h; Root from 12^h	St Vo
10 Sun	♑	○ 18^h **Pg** 18^h		E	Southern Transplanting Time	Root to 6^h; - - - -	St Vo
11 Mon	♒ 8^h	☉-☊		E/L	Southern Transplanting Time	- - - -; Flower from 8^h	
12 Tue	♒			L	Southern Transplanting Time	Flower to 23^h	St Eq
13 Wed	♓ 0^h			W	Southern Transplanting Time	Leaf from 0^h	St Vo
14 Thu	♓		☽☌♅	W	Southern Transplanting Time	Leaf to 13^h; - - - -; 19-21; - - -	
15 Fri	♈ 16^h	☋ 0^h		W/H	Southern Transplanting Time	- - - -; Leaf from 5^h to 15^h; Fruit from 16^h	Tr
16 Sat	♈			H	Southern Transplanting Time	Fruit	♄ St
17 Sun	♉ 11^h	☾ 12^h		H/E	Southern Transplanting Time	Fruit to 10^h; Root from 11^h	St Eq
18 Mon	♉			E	Southern Transplanting Time	Root	Tr
19 Tue	♉	◠ 22^h		E	Southern Transplanting Time	Root	St Vo
20 Wed	♊ 9^h			E/L	Northern Transplanting Time	Root to 8^h; Flower from 9^h	
21 Thu	♊		▲	L	Northern Transplanting Time	Flower to 8^h; Fruit from 9^h to 22^h; 23	♄ St Vo
22 Fri	♋ 17^h			L/W	Northern Transplanting Time	Flower to 16^h; Leaf from 17^h	
23 Sat	♋			W	Northern Transplanting Time	Leaf to 19^h; Fl 20^h	♄ St
24 Sun	♌ 11^h	**Ag** 6^h		W/H	Northern Transplanting Time	Flower to 10^h; Fruit from 11^h	♄ St
25 Mon	♌	● 14^h	▲	H	Northern Transplanting Time	1^h; Leaf 2^h to 12^h; Fruit from 13^h	
26 Tue	♌			H	Northern Transplanting Time	Fruit	St Vo
27 Wed	♍ 10^h			H/E	Northern Transplanting Time	Fruit to 9^h; Root from 10^h	
28 Thu	♍			E	Northern Transplanting Time	Root	
29 Fri	♍	☊ 13^h		E	Northern Transplanting Time	Root to 10^h; - - - -; Root from 17^h	St Tr
30 Sat	♍			E	Northern Transplanting Time	Root	
31 Sun	♎ 4^h		☽☌♄	E/L	Northern Transplanting Time	Rt -3^h; Flower 4^h to 14^h; - - - -	

Mercury ☿	Venus ♀	Mars ♂	Jupiter ♃	Saturn ♄	Uranus ♅	Neptune ♆	Pluto ♇
♋ 10 ♌	♊ 10 ♋	♍	♋	♎	♓	♒	♐
29 ♍	27 ♌	12 ♎			(R)	(R)	(R)

NB: All zodiac symbols refer to astronomical constellations, not astrological signs (see p.10)

Planetary aspects

(Bold = visible to naked eye)

1	♀△♄ 10^h
2	☽☍☊ 1^h ☿☌♃ 20^h ♀☍♌ 23^h
3	☽☌♂ 12^h
4	**☽•♄ 11^h**
5	
6	
7	♂△♆ 12^h
8	☽☌♇ 8^h ☉☌☿ 16^h ☿△☊ 20^h
9	☉△☊ 0^h ☽☍♀ 8^h ☽☍♃ 22^h
10	☾☍☿ 22^h
11	☾☌♆ 23^h
12	
13	
14	**☾•☊ 16^h**
15	
16	☾☍♂ 13^h ☾☍♄ 23^h
17	
18	♀☌♃ 5^h
19	☿☍♆ 4^h
20	
21	☾☍♇ 7^h ☿△♇ 19^h
22	
23	☾☌♃ 14^h
24	☾☌♀ 2^h
25	♀△☊ 10^h ♂☌♄ 20^h ☽☍♆ 22^h
26	
27	☽☌☿ 2^h
28	
29	☽☍☊ 6^h ☉☍♆ 15^h
30	
31	**☽•♄ 19^h**

Planet (naked eye) visibility
Evening: Mars, Saturn
All night:
Morning: Venus, Jupiter (from 7th)

August 2014

The Sun moves into Leo on August 11, hopefully bringing warm summer weather. Pluto is still retrograde in Sagittarius, and supports the warmth. Mercury begins the month in Cancer, moves through Leo, and on Aug 29 enters Virgo, perhaps bringing the first cool nights. Mars, having been in Virgo since November last year moves into the Light constellation of Libra on Aug 12. Together with Saturn in Libra, Neptune, retrograde in Aquarius, will reinforce the Light influences.

Jupiter in Cancer, Uranus retrograde in Pisces and, from Aug 10 to 27, Venus in Cancer will ensure precipitation. The Water influence is emphasized with three Water trines on Aug 8, 9 and 25.

Northern Transplanting Time
July 23 to Aug 7 3^h and Aug 20 1^h to Sep 3
Southern Transplanting Time
Aug 7 7^h to Aug 19 21^h

Seeds of fruit plants and **grain** to be used for seed should be harvested at Fruit times, avoiding unfavourable times (- - -). Favourable times are Aug 21 9^h to 22^h.

Immediately after harvest, sow catch crops like lupins, phacelia, mustard or wild flax.

Seeds for leaf plants: Aug 8 11^h to Aug 9 3^h, and Aug 25 2^h to 12^h.

Seeds for flower plants: Aug 1 4^h to 10^h, and at other Flower times after Aug 10.

Burn **fly papers** in the cow barn Aug 19 2^h to 6^h.

Ants in the house: burn when the Moon is in Leo, Aug 24 11^h to Aug 27 9^h.

To produce the **tree bark preparations** cut larch (for chamomile) Aug 19 2^h to 6^h, fill it and put it in the earth.

Aug

September 2014

All times in GMT

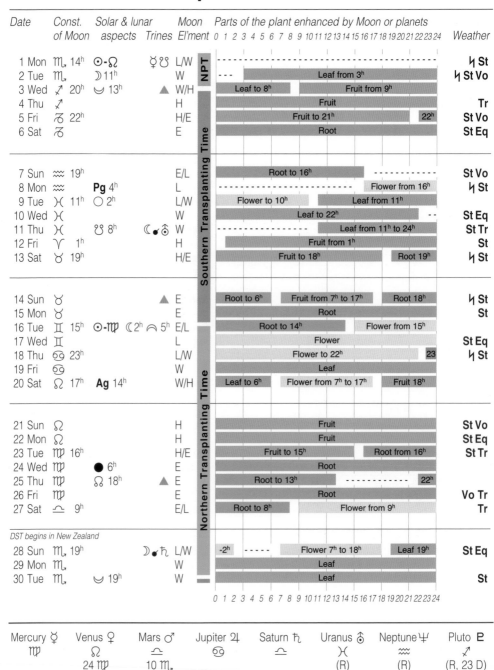

Date	Const. of Moon	Solar & lunar aspects	Moon Trines	El'ment	Parts of the plant enhanced by Moon or planets	Weather
1 Mon	♏ 14ʰ	☉-♌	☿ ☋	L/W	· ·	♄ St
2 Tue	♏	☽ 11ʰ		W	Leaf from 3ʰ	♄ St Vo
3 Wed	♐ 20ʰ	☋ 13ʰ	▲	W/H	Leaf to 8ʰ · Fruit from 9ʰ	Tr
4 Thu	♐			H	Fruit	
5 Fri	♑ 22ʰ			H/E	Fruit to 21ʰ · 22ʰ	St Vo
6 Sat	♑			E	Root	St Eq
7 Sun	♒ 19ʰ			E/L	Root to 16ʰ · · · · · · · ·	St Vo
8 Mon	♒	**Pg** 4ʰ		L	· · · · · · · · · · · · Flower from 16ʰ	♄ St
9 Tue	♓ 11ʰ	○ 2ʰ		L/W	Flower to 10ʰ · Leaf from 11ʰ	
10 Wed	♓			W	Leaf to 22ʰ · ·	St Eq
11 Thu	♓	☋ 8ʰ	☾●☋	W	· · · · · · · · · · Leaf from 11ʰ to 24ʰ	St Tr
12 Fri	♈ 1ʰ			H	Fruit from 1ʰ	St
13 Sat	♉ 19ʰ			H/E	Fruit to 18ʰ · Root 19ʰ	♄ St
14 Sun	♉		▲	E	Root to 6ʰ · Fruit from 7ʰ to 17ʰ · Root 18ʰ	♄ St
15 Mon	♉			E	Root	St
16 Tue	♊ 15ʰ	☉-♍ ☾2ʰ ☌5ʰ		E/L	Root to 14ʰ · Flower from 15ʰ	St Eq
17 Wed	♊			L	Flower	
18 Thu	♋ 23ʰ			L/W	Flower to 22ʰ · 23	♄ St
19 Fri	♋			W	Leaf	
20 Sat	♌ 17ʰ	**Ag** 14ʰ		W/H	Leaf to 6ʰ · Flower from 7ʰ to 17ʰ · Fruit 18ʰ	
21 Sun	♌			H	Fruit	St Vo
22 Mon	♌			H	Fruit	St Eq
23 Tue	♍ 16ʰ			H/E	Fruit to 15ʰ · Root from 16ʰ	St Tr
24 Wed	♍	● 6ʰ		E	Root	
25 Thu	♍	☋ 18ʰ	▲	E	Root to 13ʰ · · · · · · · 22ʰ	
26 Fri	♍			E	Root	Vo Tr
27 Sat	♎ 9ʰ			E/L	Root to 8ʰ · Flower from 9ʰ	Tr

DST begins in New Zealand

28 Sun	♏ 19ʰ	☽●♄		L/W	-2ʰ · · · · · Flower 7ʰ to 18ʰ · Leaf 19ʰ	St Eq
29 Mon	♏			W	Leaf	
30 Tue	♏	☋ 19ʰ		W	Leaf	St

Southern Transplanting Time / Northern Transplanting Time

0 1 2 3 4 5 6 7 8 9 10 11 12 13 14 15 16 17 18 19 20 21 22 23 24

Mercury ☿	Venus ♀	Mars ♂	Jupiter ♃	Saturn ♄	Uranus ♅	Neptune ♆	Pluto ♇
♍	♌	♎	♋	♎	♓	♒	♐
	24 ♍	10 ♏			(R)	(R)	(R, 23 D)

NB: All zodiac symbols refer to astronomical constellations, not astrological signs (see p.10)

Planetary aspects
(Bold = *visible to naked eye*)

1	☽☌♂ 2ʰ ☿☋ 13ʰ
2	
3	☉△♇ 16ʰ
4	☽☌♇ 17ʰ
5	
6	☽☍♃ 18ʰ
7	
8	☽☍♀ 5ʰ ☽☌♆ 9ʰ
9	
10	♀☍♆ 11ʰ ☾☍☿ 19ʰ
11	☾•☊ 1ʰ
12	
13	☿☍☊ 8ʰ ☾☍♄ 10ʰ
14	☾☍♂ 7ʰ ♀△♇ 15ʰ
15	
16	
17	☾☍♇ 13ʰ
18	
19	
20	☾☌♃ 8ʰ
21	
22	☾☍♆ 3ʰ
23	☾☌♀ 12ʰ
24	
25	☽☍☊ 10ʰ ♃△☊ 18ʰ
26	☽☌☿ 13ʰ
27	
28	☽•♄ 5ʰ
29	☽☌♂ 19ʰ
30	

Planet (naked eye) visibility
Evening: Mars, Saturn
All night:
Morning: Venus, Jupiter

September 2014

The Warmth trine on Sep 3, together with the Sun (until Sep 15) and Venus (until Sep 23) in Leo, and Pluto in Sagittarius (retrograde for the first three weeks of the month) will bring warm days. Mercury, all month in Virgo, is joined there by the Sun and Venus later in the month. This could bring cool, misty nights.

Mars in Scorpio from Sep 10, together with Jupiter in Cancer and Uranus working strongly while retrograde in Pisces, will lead to precipitation. The Light bearers are Saturn in Libra and Neptune in Aquarius, as well as Mars to Sep 10.

Northern Transplanting Time
Aug 20 to Sep 3 12ʰ
and Sep 16 8ʰ to Sep 30 18ʰ
Southern Transplanting Time
Sep 3 16ʰ to Sep 16 4ʰ and
from Sep 30 23ʰ to Oct 13

The times recommended for the **fruit harvest** are those in which the Moon is in Aries or Sagittarius. *Especially favourable:* Sep 3 9ʰ to Sep 5 21ʰ, and Sep 14 7ʰ to 17ʰ. Otherwise Sep 12 1ʰ to Sep 13 18ʰ, Sep 20 18ʰ to Sep 23 15ʰ, or other Fruit times.

The harvest of **root crops** is always best undertaken at Root times. Storage trials have demonstrated this time and again.

Good dates for **sowing winter grain** in later districts are from Sep 3 9ʰ to Sep 5 21ʰ, Sep 12 1ʰ to Sep 13 18ʰ, and other Fruit times.

Rye can if necessary also be sown at Root times with all subsequent cultivations being carried out at Fruit times.

Control ants in buildings by ashing them between Sep 3 20ʰ and Sep 5 21ʰ, or from Sep 20 17ʰ and Sep 23 15ʰ.

Slug control from Sep 18 23ʰ to Sep 20 16ʰ, or Sep 28 19ʰ to Oct 1 2ʰ.

Sep

35

October 2014

All times in GMT

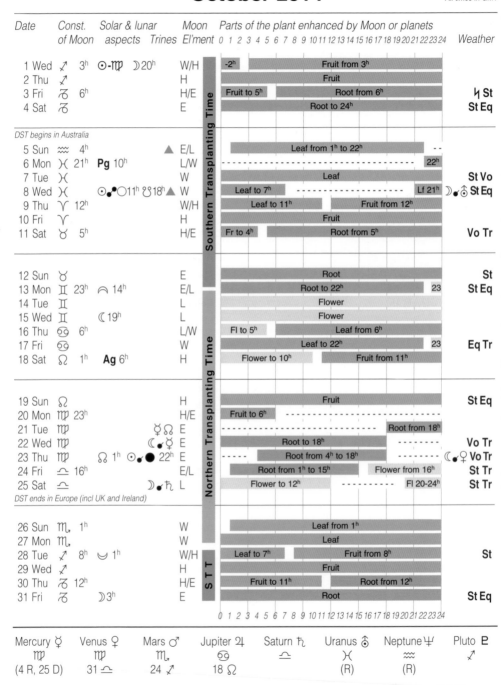

Date	Const. of Moon	Solar & lunar aspects	Trines	Moon El'ment	Transplanting time	Parts of the plant enhanced by Moon or planets (0–24)	Weather
1 Wed	♐ 3^h	⊙-♍ ☽20^h		W/H	Southern Transplanting Time	-2^h; Fruit from 3^h	
2 Thu	♐			H	Southern Transplanting Time	Fruit	
3 Fri	♑ 6^h			H/E	Southern Transplanting Time	Fruit to 5^h; Root from 6^h	♄ St
4 Sat	♑			E	Southern Transplanting Time	Root to 24^h	St Eq
DST begins in Australia							
5 Sun	♒ 4^h		▲	E/L	Southern Transplanting Time	Leaf from 1^h to 22^h - -	
6 Mon	♓ 21^h	**Pg** 10^h		L/W	Southern Transplanting Time	- - - - - - - - 22^h	
7 Tue	♓			W	Southern Transplanting Time	Leaf	St Vo
8 Wed	♓	⊙☍○11^h ☋18^h	▲	W	Southern Transplanting Time	Leaf to 7^h - - - - - - - - Lf 21^h	☽☌♅ St Eq
9 Thu	♈ 12^h			W/H	Southern Transplanting Time	Leaf to 11^h; Fruit from 12^h	
10 Fri	♈			H	Southern Transplanting Time	Fruit	
11 Sat	♉ 5^h			H/E	Southern Transplanting Time	Fr to 4^h; Root from 5^h	Vo Tr
12 Sun	♉			E	Southern Transplanting Time	Root	St
13 Mon	♊ 23^h	⌒ 14^h		E/L	Northern Transplanting Time	Root to 22^h; 23	St Eq
14 Tue	♊			L	Northern Transplanting Time	Flower	
15 Wed	♊	☾19^h		L	Northern Transplanting Time	Flower	
16 Thu	♋ 6^h			L/W	Northern Transplanting Time	Fl to 5^h; Leaf from 6^h	
17 Fri	♋			W	Northern Transplanting Time	Leaf to 22^h; 23	Eq Tr
18 Sat	♌ 1^h	**Ag** 6^h		H	Northern Transplanting Time	Flower to 10^h; Fruit from 11^h	
19 Sun	♌			H	Northern Transplanting Time	Fruit	St Eq
20 Mon	♍ 23^h			H/E	Northern Transplanting Time	Fruit to 6^h - - - - - - - -	
21 Tue	♍		☿☊	E	Northern Transplanting Time	- - - - - - - - Root from 18^h	
22 Wed	♍		☾☌☿	E	Northern Transplanting Time	Root to 18^h - - - -	Vo Tr
23 Thu	♍	☊ 1^h ⊙☌● 22^h		E	Northern Transplanting Time	- - - Root from 4^h to 18^h - - - -	☾☌♀ Vo Tr
24 Fri	♎ 16^h			E/L	Northern Transplanting Time	Root from 1^h to 15^h; Flower from 16^h	St Tr
25 Sat	♎		☽☌♄	L	Northern Transplanting Time	Flower to 12^h - - - - - Fl 20-24^h	St Tr
DST ends in Europe (incl UK and Ireland)							
26 Sun	♏ 1^h			W	Northern Transplanting Time	Leaf from 1^h	
27 Mon	♏			W	Northern Transplanting Time	Leaf	
28 Tue	♐ 8^h	⌣ 1^h		W/H	STT	Leaf to 7^h; Fruit from 8^h	St
29 Wed	♐			H	STT	Fruit	
30 Thu	♑ 12^h			H/E	STT	Fruit to 11^h; Root from 12^h	
31 Fri	♑	☽3^h		E	STT	Root	St Eq

Mercury ☿	Venus ♀	Mars ♂	Jupiter ♃	Saturn ♄	Uranus ♅	Neptune ♆	Pluto ♇
♍	♍	♏	♋	♎	♓	♒	♐
(4 R, 25 D)	31 ♎	24 ♐	18 ♌		(R)	(R)	

NB: All zodiac symbols refer to astronomical constellations, not astrological signs (see p.10)

Planetary aspects

(Bold = *visible to naked eye)*

1

2 ☽☌♇ 0^h

3

4 ☽☍♃ 11^h

5 ♂△⛢ 4^h ☽☌♆ 18^h

6

7 ☉☍⛢ 21^h

8 ☽☍♀ 3^h ☽●⛢ 10^h ♂△♃ 21^h

9 ☾☍☿ 13^h

10

11 ☾☍♄ 1^h ♀☍⛢ 9^h

12

13 ☾☍♂ 5^h

14 ☾☍♇ 21^h

15

16 ☉☌☿ 22^h

17 ☿☌♀ 18^h

18 **☾☌♃ 0^h**

19 ☾☍♆ 9^h

20

21 ☿☊ 5^h

22 ☾☍⛢ 14^h ☾●☿ 22^h

23 ☾●♀ 21^h

24

25 ☉☌♀ 8^h ☽●♄ 16^h

26

27 ♀△♆ 19^h

28 ☉△♆ 10^h **☽☌♂ 13^h**

29 ☽☌♇ 6^h

30

31

Planet (naked eye) visibility

Evening: Mars, Saturn (to 24th)

All night:

Morning: Mercury (from 23rd), Venus (to 4th), Jupiter

October 2014

Autumn has come. The Sun and Mercury are in the cool constellation of Virgo for the whole month, and Venus is there too, on all but the last day. Mars (until Oct 24) in Scorpio, Jupiter (until Oct 18) in Cancer and Uranus retrograde in Pisces support the watery influences.

From Oct 18 when Jupiter moves to Leo there could still be some fine warm days supported by Pluto in Sagittarius, and from Oct 24 Mars in Sagittarius. Saturn in Libra and Neptune in Aquarius could give rise to bright and radiant days and glowing autumn colours.

Northern Transplanting Time
Oct 13 16^h to Oct 27 23^h
Southern Transplanting Time
Sep 30 to Oct 13 12^h and
Oct 28 3^h to Nov 9

Store fruit at any Fruit time outside transplanting time. A particularly favourable time is from Oct 28 8^h to Oct 30 11^h.

All **cleared ground** should be treated with compost and sprayed with barrel preparation, and ploughed ready for winter.

Slug control from Oct 8 21^h to Oct 9 11^h, and Oct 16 6^h to Oct 17 24^h.

November 2014

All times in GMT

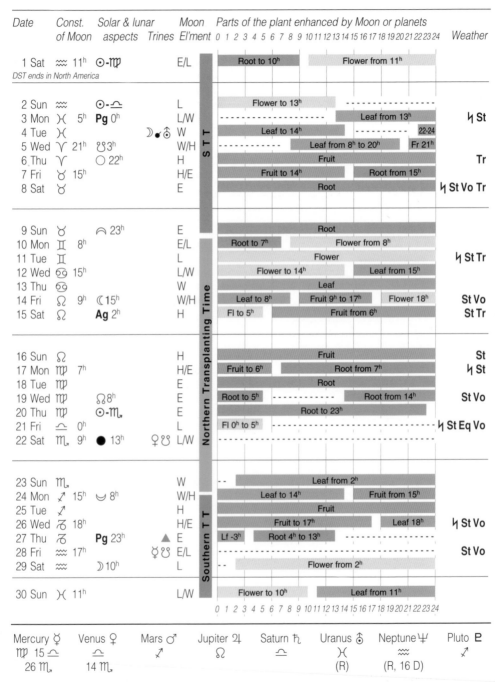

Date	Const. of Moon	Solar & lunar aspects	Trines	Moon El'ment	Parts of the plant enhanced by Moon or planets	Weather
1 Sat	♒ 11ʰ	☉-♍		E/L	Root to 10ʰ — Flower from 11ʰ	
DST ends in North America						
2 Sun	♒	☉-♎		L	Flower to 13ʰ	
3 Mon	♓ 5ʰ	Pg 0ʰ		L/W	Leaf from 13ʰ	♄ St
4 Tue	♓	☽☌♂♃		W	Leaf to 14ʰ — 22-24	
5 Wed	♈ 21ʰ	☍♄ 3ʰ		W/H	Leaf from 8ʰ to 20ʰ — Fr 21ʰ	
6 Thu	♈	○ 22ʰ		H	Fruit	Tr
7 Fri	♉ 15ʰ			H/E	Fruit to 14ʰ — Root from 15ʰ	
8 Sat	♉			E	Root	♄ St Vo Tr
9 Sun	♉	⌒ 23ʰ		E	Root	
10 Mon	♊ 8ʰ			E/L	Root to 7ʰ — Flower from 8ʰ	
11 Tue	♊			L	Flower	♄ St Tr
12 Wed	♋ 15ʰ			L/W	Flower to 14ʰ — Leaf from 15ʰ	
13 Thu	♋			W	Leaf	
14 Fri	♌ 9ʰ	☾ 15ʰ		W/H	Leaf to 8ʰ — Fruit 9ʰ to 17ʰ — Flower 18ʰ	St Vo
15 Sat	♌	Ag 2ʰ		H	Fl to 5ʰ — Fruit from 6ʰ	St Tr
16 Sun	♌			H	Fruit	St
17 Mon	♍ 7ʰ			H/E	Fruit to 6ʰ — Root from 7ʰ	♄ St
18 Tue	♍			E	Root	
19 Wed	♍	☍ 8ʰ		E	Root to 5ʰ — Root from 14ʰ	St Vo
20 Thu	♍	☉-♏		E	Root to 23ʰ	
21 Fri	♎ 0ʰ			L	Fl 0ʰ to 5ʰ	♄ St Eq Vo
22 Sat	♏ 9ʰ	● 13ʰ	♀☍	L/W		
23 Sun	♏			W	Leaf from 2ʰ	
24 Mon	♐ 15ʰ	⌣ 8ʰ		W/H	Leaf to 14ʰ — Fruit from 15ʰ	
25 Tue	♐			H	Fruit	
26 Wed	♑ 18ʰ			H/E	Fruit to 17ʰ — Leaf 18ʰ	♄ St Vo
27 Thu	♑	Pg 23ʰ	▲	E	Lf -3ʰ — Root 4ʰ to 13ʰ	
28 Fri	♒ 17ʰ		♀☍	E/L		St Vo
29 Sat	♒	☽ 10ʰ		L	Flower from 2ʰ	
30 Sun	♓ 11ʰ			L/W	Flower to 10ʰ — Leaf from 11ʰ	

0 1 2 3 4 5 6 7 8 9 10 11 12 13 14 15 16 17 18 19 20 21 22 23 24

Mercury ☿	Venus ♀	Mars ♂	Jupiter ♃	Saturn ♄	Uranus ♅	Neptune ♆	Pluto ♇
♍ 15 ♎	♎	♐	♌	♎	♓	♒	♐
26 ♏	14 ♏				(R)	(R, 16 D)	

NB: All zodiac symbols refer to astronomical constellations, not astrological signs (see p.10)

Planetary aspects
(Bold = *visible to naked eye*)

November 2014

1 ☽ ☍ ♃ 1^h

2 ☽ ☌ ♆ 1^h
3
4 ☽ ● ⊕ 18^h
5 ☽ ☍ ☿ 13^h
6
7 **☾ ☍ ♀ 5^h ☾ ☍ ♄ 16^h**
8

9
10 ♂ ☌ ♇ 23^h
11 **☾ ☍ ♇ 7^h ☾ ☍ ♂ 7^h**
12 ☿ △ ♆ 4^h
13 ♀ ☌ ♄ 1^h
14 **☾ ☌ ♃ 14^h**
15 **☾ ☍ ♆ 17^h**

16
17
18 ☉ ☌ ♄ 9^h **☾ ☍ ⊕ 21^h**
19
20
21 **☾ ☌ ☿ 18^h**
22 **☾ ☌ ♄ 6^h** ♀ ☊ 12^h

23 ☽ ☌ ♀ 2^h
24
25 ☽ ☌ ♇ 13^h
26 ☿ ☌ ♄ 3^h ☽ ☌ ♂ 8^h
27 ♀ △ ⊕ 0^h
28 ☽ ☍ ♃ 9^h ☿ ☊ 12^h
29 ☽ ☌ ♆ 6^h

30

Planet (naked eye) visibility
Evening: Mars
All night:
Morning: Mercury (to 21st), Jupiter

In the darkness of November there is still hope for some Light impulses. Saturn is in Libra, the Sun too from Nov 2 to Nov 19, and Neptune is in Aquarius. Venus begins the month in Libra, but then moves to watery Scorpio on Nov 14, where Mercury joins Venus on Nov 26. Uranus in Pisces, and from Nov 20 the Sun in Scorpio, reinforce precipitation which may come as rain or snow. Mars and Pluto in Sagittarius and Jupiter in Leo could mediate some warmth. November may have some wonderful weather.

Northern Transplanting Time
Nov 10 2^h to Nov 24 7^h
Southern Transplanting Time
Oct 28 to Nov 9 21^h and Nov 24 11^h to Dec 7

The Flower times in Transplanting Time (from Nov 10 8^h to Nov 12 14^h, from Nov 14 18^h to Nov 15 5^h and Nov 21 0^h to 5^h) are ideal for **planting flower bulbs,** showing vigorous growth and vivid colours. The remaining Flower times should only be considered as back up, as bulbs planted on those times will not flower so freely.

If not already completed in October, all organic waste materials should be gathered and made into a **compost.** Applying the biodynamic preparations to the compost will ensure a rapid transformation and good fungal development. An application of barrel preparation will also help the composting process.

Fruit and forest trees will also benefit at this time from a spraying of horn manure and/or barrel preparation when being transplanted.

Best times for **cutting Advent greenery** and **Christmas trees** for transporting are Nov 24 15^h to Nov 26 17^h, & Nov 28 16^h to Nov 30 10^h. When cutting trees avoid unfavourable times (- - -).

Burn **fly papers** in cow barn Nov 5 19^h to Nov 7 14^h.

For biodynamic **tree bark preparations** put birch wood (with yarrow) into the earth on Nov 5 23^h to Nov 7 14^h.

Nov

December 2014

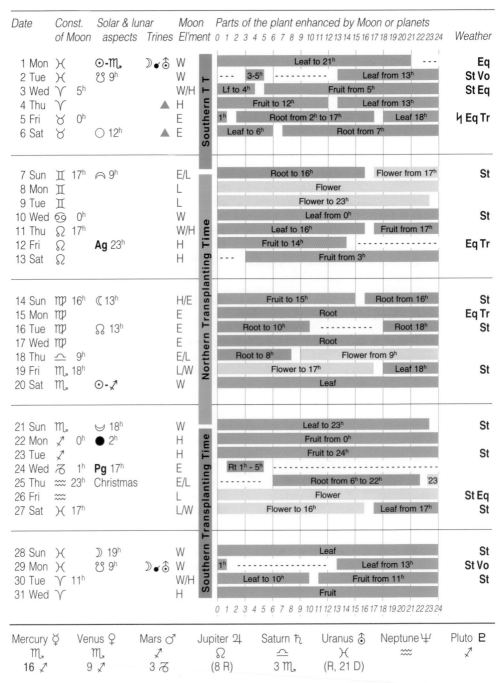

Date	Const. of Moon	Solar & lunar aspects	Moon Trines	El'ment	Parts of the plant enhanced by Moon or planets	Weather

Southern TT

1 Mon ♓		☉-♏	☽•☌	W	Leaf to 21ʰ · · ·	Eq
2 Tue ♓		☊ 9ʰ		W	· · · 3-5ʰ · · · · · · · · · · Leaf from 13ʰ	St Vo
3 Wed ♈ 5ʰ				W/H	Lf to 4ʰ Fruit from 5ʰ	St Eq
4 Thu ♈			▲	H	Fruit to 12ʰ Leaf from 13ʰ	
5 Fri ♉ 0ʰ				E	1ʰ Root from 2ʰ to 17ʰ Leaf 18ʰ	♄ Eq Tr
6 Sat ♉		○ 12ʰ	▲	E	Leaf to 6ʰ Root from 7ʰ	

Northern Transplanting Time

7 Sun ♊ 17ʰ		⌒ 9ʰ		E/L	Root to 16ʰ Flower from 17ʰ	St
8 Mon ♊				L	Flower	
9 Tue ♊				L	Flower to 23ʰ	
10 Wed ♋ 0ʰ				W	Leaf from 0ʰ	St
11 Thu ♌ 17ʰ				W/H	Leaf to 16ʰ Fruit from 17ʰ	
12 Fri ♌		Ag 23ʰ		H	Fruit to 14ʰ · · · · · · · · ·	Eq Tr
13 Sat ♌				H	· · · Fruit from 3ʰ	

14 Sun ♍ 16ʰ		☾ 13ʰ		H/E	Fruit to 15ʰ Root from 16ʰ	St
15 Mon ♍				E	Root	Eq Tr
16 Tue ♍		☍ 13ʰ		E	Root to 10ʰ · · · · · · · · · · Root 18ʰ	St
17 Wed ♍				E	Root	
18 Thu ♎ 9ʰ				E/L	Root to 8ʰ Flower from 9ʰ	
19 Fri ♏ 18ʰ				L/W	Flower to 17ʰ Leaf 18ʰ	St
20 Sat ♏		☉-♐		W	Leaf	

Southern Transplanting Time

21 Sun ♏		☽ 18ʰ		W	Leaf to 23ʰ	St
22 Mon ♐ 0ʰ		● 2ʰ		H	Fruit from 0ʰ	
23 Tue ♐				H	Fruit to 24ʰ	St
24 Wed ♑ 1ʰ		Pg 17ʰ		E	Rt 1ʰ - 5ʰ · · · · · · · · · · · · · ·	
25 Thu ♒ 23ʰ		Christmas		E/L	· · · · · · · · Root from 6ʰ to 22ʰ 23	St Eq
26 Fri ♒				L	Flower	
27 Sat ♓ 17ʰ				L/W	Flower to 16ʰ Leaf from 17ʰ	St

28 Sun ♓		☽ 19ʰ		W	Leaf	St
29 Mon ♓		☊ 9ʰ	☽•☌	W	1ʰ · · · · · · · · · · · · · · · · · Leaf from 13ʰ	St Vo
30 Tue ♈ 11ʰ				W/H	Leaf to 10ʰ Fruit from 11ʰ	St
31 Wed ♈				H	Fruit	

0 1 2 3 4 5 6 7 8 9 10 11 12 13 14 15 16 17 18 19 20 21 22 23 24

| Mercury ☿ ♏ 16 ♐ | Venus ♀ ♏ 9 ♐ | Mars ♂ ♐ 3 ♑ | Jupiter ♃ ♌ (8 R) | Saturn ♄ ♎ 3 ♏ | Uranus ⛢ ♓ (R, 21 D) | Neptune ♆ ♒ | Pluto ♇ ♐ |

NB: All zodiac symbols refer to astronomical constellations, not astrological signs (see p.10)

Planetary aspects

(Bold = visible to naked eye)

1 ☽•⚷ 23ʰ
2
3
4 ♀△♃ 19ʰ ☉△⚷ 22ʰ
5 ☽♂♄ 7ʰ
6 ☿△⚷ 4ʰ ☽♂☿ 10ʰ

7 ☾☌♀ 10ʰ
8 ☉♂☿ 10ʰ ☾☌♇ 17ʰ
9
10 ☾☌♂ 12ʰ
11
12 ☾☌♃ 0ʰ ☿△♃ 11ʰ
13 ☾☌♅ 1ʰ

14 ☉△♃ 16ʰ
15
16 ☾☌⚷ 5ʰ
17
18
19 ☾☌♄ 21ʰ
20 ♀☌♇ 21ʰ

21
22 ☽☌☿ 16ʰ ☽☌♇ 23ʰ
23 ☽☌♀ 3ʰ
24
25 ☽☌♂ 5ʰ ☿☌♇ 7ʰ ☽☌♃ 15ʰ
26 ☽☌♅ 13ʰ
27

28
29 ☽•⚷ 4ʰ
30
31

Two Water trines on Dec 4 and 6 may bring precipitation. Until Dec 19 the Sun is in watery Scorpio. Mercury and Venus begin the month also in Scorpio, but like the Sun move on to the Warmth constellation of Sagittarius. Pluto in Sagittarius and Jupiter in Leo bring Warmth influences throughout the month, strengthened by Jupiter's retrograde motion from Dec 8.

On Dec 3 Mars moves into the cool Earth constellation of Capricorn. Saturn in Libra and Neptune in Aquarius bring Light influences, perhaps sunny winter days.

Northern Transplanting Time
Dec 7 11ʰ to Dec 21 17ʰ
Southern Transplanting Time
Nov 24 to Dec 7 7ʰ and Dec 21 21ʰ to Jan 3

The transplanting time is good for **pruning trees and hedges.** Fruit trees should be pruned at Fruit times.

Burn feathers or skins of **warm blooded pests** from Dec 6 4ʰ to 5ʰ. This time is very short. Ensure the fire is glowing hot by 4ʰ and that the process is completed by 5ʰ.

Best times for cutting **Advent greenery** and **Christmas trees** are at Flower times to ensure lasting fragrance.

Southern hemisphere:
Control slugs Nov 30 23ʰ to Dec 1 21ʰ, Dec 10 0ʰ to Dec 11 16ʰ (Dec 10 particularly good).
Harvest time for seeds:
Leaf seeds: Leaf times from Dec10.
Fruit seeds: Fruit times from Dec 11.
Root seeds: Root times from Dec 14.
Flower seeds: Flower times from Dec 18.

Planet (naked eye) visibility
Evening: Venus (from 5th), Mars
All night: Jupiter
Morning: Saturn (from 2nd)

*We would like to wish all our readers
a blessed Advent and Christmastide
and good health for the New Year of 2015*

Sowing times for trees and shrubs

Jan 1: Alder, Apple, Beech
Jan 5: Apple, Ash, Beech, Sweet chestnut
Jan 31: Apple, Beech, Maple, Sweet chestnut
April 8: Ash, Fir, Hazel, Horse chestnut, Oak,
  Pine, Spruce, Yew
April 16: Alder, Cherry, Oak, Yew
April 21: Apple, Beech, Maple, Sweet chestnut
April 23: Cherry, Horse chestnut, Sweet chestnut
May 3: Elm, Juniper, Pine, Thuja
May 10: Ash, Cedar, Fir, Hazel, Hornbeam, Plum,
  Spruce, Thuja
May 11: Birch, Oak, Pear, Yew
June 13: Birch, Lime, Pear, Robinia, Willow
June 25: Cherry, Horse chestnut, Oak, Sweet
  chestnut, Yew
July 4: Ash, Cedar, Fir, Hazel, Spruce
July 22: Beech, Lime, Pear
July 28: Birch, Pear
Aug 19: Alder, Elm, Larch, Lime
Aug 29: Ash, Cedar, Fir, Hazel, Spruce,
Sep 10: Birch, Pear
Sep 13: Larch, Lime
Oct 7: Ash, Cedar, Fir, Hazel, Spruce
Oct 11: Birch, Lime, Pear, Robinia, Willow

The above dates refer to sowing times when the seeds of trees and shrubs are put in the earth. They are not times for transplanting already existing plants.

The dates given are based on planetary aspects, which create particularly favourable growing conditions for the species in question.

For trees and shrubs not mentioned above, there are no particular times for sowing this year. Sow at an appropriate time of the Moon's position in the zodiac, depending on the part of the tree or shrub to be enhanced.

Felling times for timber

Feb 15: Ash, Cedar, Cherry, Fir, Hazel, Spruce
Feb 16: Alder, Elm, Larch, Lime, Sweet chestnut
March 1: Apple, Ash, Beech, Hazel, Spruce, Sweet
  chestnut
March 13: Ash, Hazel, Hornbeam, Spruce
March 14: Alder, Ash, Horse chestnut, Pine, Yew
March 26: Apple, Sweet chestnut
March 29: Birch, Pear, Robinia
April 3: Elm, Fir, Larch, Lime, Juniper, Thuja
April 18: Walnut, Willow
April 29: Larch, Lime
May 4: Ash, Cedar, Fir, Spruce *(esp. good)*
May 12: Alder, Cherry, Larch, Lime, Oak, Yew
May 31: Ash, Cedar, Fir, Spruce, Sweet chestnut
June 29: Cedar, Fir
July 19: Alder, Elm, Larch, Lime
July 24: Birch, Pear
July 25: Alder, Elm, Larch, Lime
Aug 1: Birch, Larch, Pear, Pine
Aug 7: Sweet chestnut
Aug 8: Larch, Lime
Aug 21: Larch, Lime
Aug 25: Birch, Larch, Lime, Pear, Robinia, Willow
Sep 3: Fir *(esp. good)*
Sep 14: Willow *(esp. good)*
Sep 25: Apple, Sweet chestnut
Oct 8: Apple, Cherry, Sweet chestnut
Oct 14: Cedar, Hazel, Spruce, Sweet chestnut
Oct 27: Birch, Pear, Robinia
Oct 28: Ash, Cedar, Fir, Hazel, Spruce
Dec 6: Alder , Elm, Larch, Lime
Dec 12: Apple, Larch, Lime, Sweet chestnut
Dec 14: Apple, Ash, Hazel, Pear, Spruce, Sweet
  chestnut *(esp. good)*

Those trees which are not listed should be felled during November and December on Flower days during the descending Moon period (transplanting time).

Fungal problems

The function of fungus in nature is to break down dying organic materials. It appears amongst our crops when unripe manure compost or uncomposted animal by-products such as horn and bone meal are used but also when seeds are harvested during unfavourable constellations: according to Steiner, 'When Moon forces are working too strongly on the Earth ...'

Tea can be made from horsetail *(Equisetum arvense)* and sprayed on to the soil where affected plants are growing. This draws the fungal level back down into the ground where it belongs.

The plants can be strengthened by spraying stinging nettle tea on the leaves. This will promote good assimilation, stimulate the flow of sap and help fungal diseases to disappear.

Biodynamic preparation plants

Pick **dandelions** in the morning on Flower days as soon as they are open and while the centre of the flowers are still tightly packed. Pick **yarrow** on Fruit days when the Sun is in Leo (around middle of August). Pick **chamomile** on Flower days just before midsummer. If they are harvested too late, seeds will begin to form and there are often grubs in the hollow heads. Collect **stinging nettles** when the first flowers are opening, usually around midsummer. Harvest the whole plants without roots on Flower days. Pick **valerian** on Flower days around midsummer. All the flowers (except valerian) should be laid out on paper and dried in the shade.

Collect **oak bark** on Root days. The pithy material below the bark should not be used.

The care of bees

A colony of bees lives in its hive closed off from the outside world. For extra protection against harmful influences, the inside of the hive is sealed with propolis. The link with the wider surroundings is made by the bees which fly in and out of the hive.

To make good use of cosmic rhythms, the beekeeper needs to create the right conditions in much the same way as the gardener or farmer does with the plants.

The gardener works the soil and in so doing allows cosmic forces to penetrate it via the air. These forces can then be taken up and used by the plants until the soil is next moved.

When the beekeeper opens up the hive, the sealing layer of propolis is broken. This creates a disturbance as a result of which cosmic forces can enter and influence the life of the hive until the next intervention by the beekeeper. By this means the beekeeper can directly mediate cosmic forces to his bees.

It is not insignificant which forces of the universe are brought into play when the the the hive is opened. The beekeeper can consciously intervene by choosing days for working with the hive that will help the colony to develop and build up its food reserves. The bees will then reward the beekeeper by providing a portion of their harvest in the form of honey.

Earth-Root days can be selected for opening the hive if the bees need to do more building. Light-Flower days encourage brood activity and colony development. Warmth-Fruit days stimulate the collection of nectar. Water-Leaf days are unsuitable for working in the hive or for the removal and processing of honey.

Since the late 1970s the varroa mite has affected virtually every bee colony in Europe. Following a number of comparative trials we recommend burning and making an ash of the varroa mite in the usual way. After dynamizing it for one hour, the ash should be put in a salt-cellar and sprinkled lightly between the combs. The ash should be made and sprinkled when the Sun and Moon are in Taurus.

Feeding bees in preparation for winter

The herbal teas recommended as supplements in the feeding of bees prior to winter are all plants that have proved their value over many years. Yarrow, chamomile, dandelion and valerian are made by pouring boiling water over the flowers, allowing them to brew for fifteen minutes and then straining them. Stinging nettle, horsetail and oak bark are placed in cold water, brought slowly to the boil and simmered for fifteen minutes. Three grams of each dried herb and half a litre of the prepared teas is enough to produce 100 litres of liquid feed. This is a particularly important treatment in years when there are large amounts of honeydew.

Since one focus of this calendar is on the saving and production of seeds it might have been appropriate to describe the swarming and reproduction of bees too. But this subject was described in some depth last year. Instead we would like to respond to several requests and direct your attention to the special 'swarm catcher bag' which every beekeeper should have to hand, especially those whose hives are kept in orchards or woodland. Its construction with an extendible pole allows the beekeeper to catch swarms in places that would otherwise require skilled ladder work. The open bag is held beneath the swarm and the branch is given a sharp tap. The bees fall into the bag that can then be closed by pulling on the cord attached to it.

The most favourable dates for growing queen bees from worker cells this year occur in June. If the breeding of queens needs to start earlier it is best to choose Flower days. The young mated queens from the June breeding should be kept with the mating nuclei because young queens introduced to a hive so late in the season are likely to be more prone to disease the following year.

User Report from Egypt

Ibrahim Abouleish and Angela Hofmann

In Egypt we have developed the following system in our biodynamic work: we use the times recommended in the *Maria Thun Calendar* for sowing seed, for spraying horn manure (either immediately after sowing while the field is being irrigated, or later as soon as it can be walked or driven on), and for spraying horn silica three times in succession when the Moon is in one of the three constellations of the appropriate trine, starting when the plants have developed their third true leaves.

We have carried out trials on this and can confirm the positive effect of choosing the right time. Here are some descriptions and results of the trials.

Potatoes with horn silica spray

The potatoes were all planted on the same day and treated with horn manure. Once the second pair of leaves had fully unfolded half of the field was sprayed with horn silica on three successive Root periods (Nov 11, 22, 29, 2003). On Nov 22 the plants were also hoed. When the crop was harvested, the section of the field which had received horn silica had a significantly higher yield. The difference in taste and conformation was marked and during storage at a temperature of 4°C there was a big difference in quality.

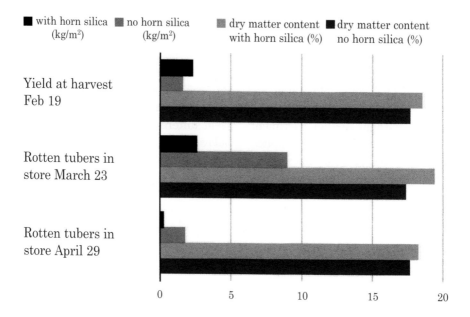

■ with horn silica (kg/m²)　■ no horn silica (kg/m²)　■ dry matter content with horn silica (%)　■ dry matter content no horn silica (%)

Yield at harvest Feb 19

Rotten tubers in store March 23

Rotten tubers in store April 29

0　　5　　10　　15　　20

Yield and storage of potatoes with horn silica spray

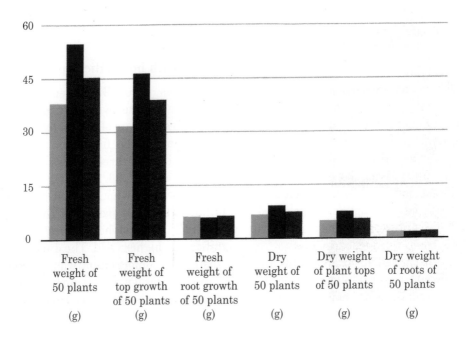

Legend:
■ no horn silica ■ horn silica at Leaf times ■ horn silica at Root times

| Fresh weight of 50 plants (g) | Fresh weight of top growth of 50 plants (g) | Fresh weight of root growth of 50 plants (g) | Dry weight of 50 plants (g) | Dry weight of plant tops of 50 plants (g) | Dry weight of roots of 50 plants (g) |

Yield of Egyptian clover with horn silica

Egyptian clover with horn silica

The clover was all sown at a Leaf time and treated with horn manure. One section was then left without further treatment, another section received three applications of horn silica at Leaf times and a third was treated three times with horn silica at Root times.

Anise crop

We treated our anise crop in different ways and were able to observe significant yield differences, as shown in the table below.

Anise	*Variant 1*	*Variant 2*	*Variant 3*
Sowing time	Fruit time	Fruit time	Flower time
Horn manure spray	–	Fruit time	Flower time
Horn silica spray	–	3 × at Fruit times	3 × at Flower times
Harvest	Fruit time	Fruit time	Flower time
Yield	450 kg	564 kg	480 kg

Dawn over Sekem Guesthouse

Our Visits to Sekem

Matthias Thun

In the late summer of 1997 Maria Thun gave a lecture in Munich about her research. During her presentation she also spoke about the observations she had made of the fine sand forms on the west coast of the island of Sylt. There, one spring as the sea water was ebbing away, she saw wonderful forms develop in the sand. These changed once the Moon had moved into another constellation. We could confirm this observation in the autumn when we visited the island again.

At the end of the lecture my mother was approached by a couple called Brand. They were so inspired by the presentation that they managed to persuade her

to visit Sekem in the Egyptian desert and share this experience with them.

The former biodynamic consultant for the Mediterranean region and also Sekem, Georg Merckens, had tried several times to invite Maria Thun to Sekem. She always turned it down on the grounds that the climate was too hot for her.

Dr Brand was a dentist and familiar with the founding story of Sekem having set up the dentistry department in the medical centre there. The medical centre came about through the initiative of Dr Hans Werner and is where the residents of the nearby villages are treated. On November 17, 1997, on the day of the bomb

47

attack near Luxor, we were due to fly to Cairo. At the airport in Munich we were 'met' at the Egyptian Airlines stand by radio and television journalists intent on dissuading us from travelling – which they didn't succeed in doing.

When we then landed in Cairo in an almost empty plane, the trepidation of my mother was immediately confirmed. Although it was November and night had fallen when we stepped out of the air-conditioned plane, we met a blast of heat so strong it took our breath away.

After a speedy passage through customs and a 45 minute taxi ride through the desert we arrived at the Sekem farm. We were met with a delicious evening meal and tried to spend the rest of the night in the not-yet-air-conditioned guest house.

My mother always got up early, so at 5.30 we set out alone on a walk across part of the farm. It wasn't at all what we expected a farm in the desert to be like. It was an oasis of vibrant vitality and growth that totally overwhelmed us.

After a very warm welcome by Ibra-him Abouleish and his colleagues, the Sekem day began at 7 o'clock. Maria Thun was faced with a big question and certain amount of scepticism. How can the cosmic forces become effective in this sandy soil? She knew from her planting trials that only when at least 1.4% available humus is present can cosmic influences be effective.

She had had this same experience at the beginning of the 1950s in her three gardens in Marburg. (One, a former market garden, in an east-west direction, another with low humus content in a south-westerly direction, and the third garden lay in a north-easterly direction dominated by shade; all the gardens had sandy soil and yet had very different characteristics due to aspect and compost variability.) She had also experienced sandy soil on her parents' farm and much later on the island of Sylt on a farm with a soil of loamy sand.

As we walked across the farm we were continually met with something new and surprising. Around all the fields tree hedges, since grown into avenues, had been planted. Each open area was surrounded by an ingenious ditch-based irrigation system that created an excellent micro-climate and contributed to the formation of a heavy dew. The necessary

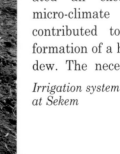

Irrigation system at Sekem

Maria Thun giving advice on site at Sekem

soil humus was provided for not only by the roots of crops left in the soil but also copious amounts of compost. This compost came from a generously laid-out compost area which, depending on the Sun's position, also had sufficient shade. This composting set up was created initially by the gardener Frieda Gögler and then further developed by Georg Merckens. The compost is made up of plant-based materials and manures from cows, water buffalo, camels, goats and hens.

My mother found peace as soon as she saw this composting site because she knew immediately that the cosmos would be able to work in soil treated with such compost material.

Another question that my mother was concerned with was that of water. Early on in her research work she had found that when plants are irrigated, the influence of the sidereal Moon grows weaker and those of the Moon's phases become stronger. Following further investigation

and an explanation by Klaus Merckens these concerns too were cleared up. In the early years of the farm the fields were watered with overhead irrigation and this very quickly led to a build-up of salt deposits in the soil. Then a version of the ancient trickle irrigation system was developed. This allows water to run through narrow ditches, 40 cm (16 in) wide, then by ingeniously damming the water on the almost level areas, the water is allowed to trickle slowly into the soil without any deposition of salt.

Angela Hoffmann has been involved with all the work that has been carried out since the farm was founded. Together with Klaus Merckens she worked to ensure that we could gain a full and diverse impression of their work with the farm.

We visited the farm several times in the years leading up to 2004, in order to accompany the research work that had started there.

Isis Medicine

Astrid Engelbrecht, MD

Maria Thun contributed in a significant way not only to agriculture but also to the further development of anthroposophical medicine.

Anthroposophical medicine came into existence about a hundred years ago through the close cooperation of Rudolf Steiner and the physician Ita Wegman. Through his capacity for supersensible perception, Steiner was able to build on the hidden wisdom of ancient times, developing it further through his own research.

Ita Wegman, his close co-worker in the field of medicine over many years, founded her own clinic in Arlesheim, Switzerland, in 1921, not far from Dornach where Steiner was living. This is where she started using the new anthroposophical remedies, often with astounding results. She continued working closely with Steiner until his death in 1925. The medicines and the way illnesses were treated were adjusted as necessary. The new approach to medicine based on the results of Steiner's spiritual research was, in this way, thoroughly and intensively worked through in a practical and concrete way during Steiner's last years.

Even today some hundred years later the key principles and practices hold true. At the same time it is clear that new ways are needed of addressing the changed life situations of today. Even if treatments prove successful, which happily they still do, there are frequently situations in which the medicines no longer appear to have the effect they once had. This is why anthroposophical medicine today is sometimes referred to as complementary medicine. This means that it is complementary to, or is an extension of, standard medical treatment. This is the situation today, but it is certainly not what Steiner and Wegman originally intended. They wanted a real alternative to standard medicine, one which based itself on a spiritual as well as a physical understanding of the human being.

The nature of illness has changed considerably since Steiner's time. The emphasis has shifted from infectious illnesses and inflammations towards more chronic and degenerative diseases. Illnesses affecting the immune system have also increased, especially in the last decades – from food allergies and allergic skin conditions through to autoimmune diseases where the organs or joints are destroyed by the body's own immune system: it is the body that is attacking itself from within. We also have completely new illnesses like Lyme disease or AIDS. The human constitution has also changed.

It becomes clear from all this that in order to reconnect with the founding intentions, the original spiritual insights need to relate more directly with today's changed living conditions. Further work and research on the development of remedies is needed including the harnessing of cosmic forces in the way Maria Thun has done for agriculture.

This is what stands behind the Isis impulse. The Isis Foundation for Contemporary Medicine was founded in Hamburg in 2008. Though the Isis Foundation currently concerns itself with therapeutic issues, it is in no way limited to these and could also be supportive in other fields of life. It is set up in such a way as to have broad relevance for the existential questions of our time such as how the living foundations for human life on earth and its social context can be renewed.

The use of the name Isis may seem strange since it reminds one of the ancient Egyptian goddess. Isis as a spiritual being, however, also has meaning for our time and for the future. All ancient cultures and religions had highly revered female deities connected with life. They reflect the coming into being, growth and fertility of the earth. In the Christian tradition this role was represented by Mary before it was repressed by conventional church tradition.

The quotation from Goethe, 'the eternal feminine draws us on,' directs our attention towards the primal power of the feminine, a power imbued with spiritual force. This archetypal feminine principle appears in nature and in her physical matter. The substances of the earth at their core are just as good and divine as the non-material and purely spiritual. They have also arisen from the spirit.

In contrast, there is a school of thought in our culture that ranks the ideal, the invisible spirit, as being of a higher order than matter, and matter is considered of less value than spirit because it hinders the development of spirit. Such an attitude leads ultimately to asceticism, denial of the world and self-denial.

Goethe clearly saw this differently, and the Isis Foundation too builds on the understanding that spirit and matter have equal validity and need each other. It follows from this that cosmic laws are active within earthly material processes and that everything we do on the earth has a connection to the forces of the cosmos. These were the thoughts that led Maria Thun to link the care of the earth and its creatures with the planets and stars.

With the Isis remedies, the healing effect of a particular substance is also made more effective when these cosmic forces are used in the process of preparing them. When preparing medicinal remedies, other more specific aspects need to be considered as well as those published in the *Calendar*.

When it flowers, the light qualities of a plant are expressed most clearly and therefore have a correspondence with the Flower times. At such times the Moon is moving through a Light constellation. Through its mediation these cosmic light forces are directed down and strengthen the earth's own light forces. Similar effects also come about with, for example, certain planetary aspects. At such times the elemental beings active in the light feel particularly well and work in a harmonious way on the material and etheric creation of the blossoms.

A flower picked at a Light or Flower time contains powerful, healing light forces which can be used for treating human beings. This is very important because a lack of light forces is the cause of many prevalent physical complaints today including problems with the spine, the skin or the inner organs.

The moment in which mineral, plant or animal matter is removed from its natural context is like an open window to the forces of the cosmos. The position of the stars is imprinted on it at that particular moment. It is like the horoscope of the birth of a human being.

A further important step in post-harvest preparation is that of potentising (rhythmic dilution) which must also be carried out in the right constellation. Those who are practised in pontentisation can experience the influence of that particular day's planetary aspects. It is very special when someone is able directly to experience what is written in the *Calendar*. It is also possible to experience, during the process of potentisation, how the influence of the planetary aspects gradually builds from potency to potency.

Returning to the example of the flower. A new remedy is currently being created from the petals of the white rose and sodium silicate solution (also known as waterglass). It is potentised alternately during the three Light constellations of Aquarius, Gemini and Libra with only one potency being produced each day. Each of the light constellations has a somewhat different quality. These subtle differences are brought into the remedy consistently and evenly by adhering strictly to the sequence of Light constellations. The same principle is observed in producing the sodium silicate solution and in picking the rose blossom.

At this point we can see that the varying qualities of the three light constel-

52

lations are applied in a more differentiated way when making remedies than they are in agriculture. In principle there is no reason why these subtle differences could not also be experienced in relation to agriculture.

In the completed sodium silicate/white rose preparation which exists in different potencies, one can experience inwardly how the light forces are carried into the whole nervous system. The brain is refreshed and memory and thinking capacities are reinvigorated. The vegetative nerve system also regenerates itself, the person has more energy and can more easily limit stress and nervousness. The light forces also help harmful influences to be more readily recognised and thereby also held in check.

During Isis research we are often very surprised how strongly the cosmic influences imprint themselves in the medicine and how positive the effect is in practice. In the application of these remedies, whether by doctors or the patients themselves, the psychological or physical problems are addressed in a much deeper and more fundamental way than if the cosmic components were not present. During the Isis training courses, knowledge is shared and meditative perception is schooled.

With regard to the flower I can also work with other important qualities. If I want to influence the lymphatic and fluid systems of the body then I potentise at a time when the Moon mediates watery influences, at a Leaf time. Warmth, which is needed for the treatment of heart problems, can be found via Fruit times. For the Earth quality, needed to encourage stability and clarity, I would choose Root times for my potentising. During the last ten years of development a whole range of medicines have been developed and are now available through pharmacies.

At this point I would like to once again acknowledge and express my appreciation for Maria Thun's life work. She opened a new gateway to life that extends way beyond gardening and farming. She researched the connection between the earth and the healing forces of the cosmos using her deep intuitive power and gave them practical application.

It is not surprising that the Moon plays such a key role. It is outwardly the largest visible heavenly body after the Sun and has a lot of influence on the earth as can be seen in the changing tides or the female menstrual cycle. Already in ancient times there were centres of learning that explored the secrets of the Moon. Steiner described how such a pre-Christian mystery centre once existed at Ephesus in Asia Minor in which Artemis, the Moon goddess, was revered. The priestesses dedicated themselves to the Moon through whom they could study the cosmos with its angels and gods. This Moon wisdom was very important for the culture of the time: buildings were created, harvest was set and festivals were celebrated according to it. The king also sought guidance in the leadership of his people from these Moon mystery centres, the sick were healed there, and they were ultimately important for the birth of anthroposophy.

Along with these Moon mysteries were also centres of learning that explored the Sun mysteries and which took the Sun as their source of inspiration. These centres are connected with Christ. Since Christ is the central figure in earth evolution these centres of learning are also of great importance. Steiner places his work and his path to spiritual knowledge in this context. The striving for pure spirit, for spiritual truth living in the immaterial spiritual world, was the field of his activity.

The Sun path can be seen as having a more masculine orientation while that of the Moon is more feminine. In order to be born in a physical body, Christ also needed a mother. Here we can see in a very simple way that the Sun mysteries do not stand opposed to the Moon mysteries. The two paths are not alternatives but need each other just as day needs night. They have, as described above, different areas of work. The wisdom living in substance, in earthly existence, is unlocked through the feminine path.

The Christian path, as the Sun path, cannot thrive and develop without the input of the Moon path. The wisdom of the Moon prepares the way and enables the Sun wisdom to be fruitful on earth. Out of this polarity between the two arises the possibility for being creative and for freedom. Ita Wegman's work arose from the Moon mysteries. The Isis impulse has the same source. In her life's work Maria Thun made a significant contribution in unlocking the wisdom connected with the Moon mysteries and presenting it in a modern form.

Maria Thun, Healing and Anthroposophical Medicine

Matthias Thun

During the question and answer sessions that usually followed Maria Thun's lectures there was often amazement about the wide range of themes contained in her presentations. Her interest in the various healing methods went right back to her childhood.

She grew up on a small farm on which all family members had to work. The only day in the week when no work was expected was Sunday. In the morning the cows, pigs and poultry were fed. Afterwards came church. After lunch, if the weather was fine, there was a leisurely walk. This, however, was essentially a walk around the farm to see how the harvest was developing in the field. My mother's godmother always joined in this walk and she knew all about the herbs that grew along the paths and on the fields. She was very keen on showing these herbs to the children and explaining their healing effects on animals and humans.

Maria's interest in herbs was thus awakened very early on. Later, when she was about fourteen years old, she shared her knowledge with various groups of interested women who were collecting medicinal plants for hospitals. The hospitals used them to make various teas.

When my mother settled with her family in Marburg in 1945 she was able to establish three small gardens. There she began not only her initial research into cosmic rhythms but also grew many herbs. During this time she also made observations concerning the formation of dew.

Her mother had already shown her as a child how something of the day's weather could be read in the dew. Thus if the morning dew was heavy the day would be sunny and dry. But if there was no dew then one would have to reckon on rain.

Having strengthened her ability to observe closely through her planetary and star research, she started observing the formation of dew in relation to the Moon and zodiac constellations. She discovered that not only did dew drops differ greatly in size but that the clarity of form and colouration of the surrounding plants reflected in the dew drops also varied greatly. There were also days when Maria Thun noticed that the dew had 'no wish'

A dewdrop

to be reflective and was therefore almost silvery grey in appearance.

Around the mid-1960s Maria Thun was invited to give a lecture in Eckwälden. There she spoke about her research and the observations she had made about dew development. Among her listeners was Dr Rudolf Hauschka, the founder of the Wala medicine firm. He was enthused. He had done a lot of research to find out the best way of keeping plant juices fresh. He had on the one hand investigated rhythmic stirring and on the other tried using dew. At the request of Rudolf Hauschka, Maria Thun stayed for a few days in Eckwälden in order to find confirmation of the link between the constellations and dew formation. Thus began an active period of cooperation between the two which proved very fruitful for both.

Maria Thun formed two study groups within the Marburg Biodynamic

Dr Hartmut Ramm and Maria Thun at the mistletoe garden of the Hiscia Institute, Arlesheim, Switzerland

Top: Mature mistletoe

Below: Young mistletoe on fir

Group. In one, horticultural and agricultural themes were taken up; in the other, anthroposophy. She had already started her weed trials by that time. Rudolf Steiner indicated in the Agriculture Course that weeds could be regulated (but not altogether destroyed) by burning and making ash of their seeds. Because the issue of weed control in agriculture and horticulture was always a lively discussion point, she set up some extensive trials. It soon became clear that very little ash was produced and so she decided to make use of the Hahnemann potentising method. In the trials it was not only the pure ash that was used but also each of the decimal (D) potencies produced from

it, right up to D36. The results showed that each of the applied potencies brought about differences in the plant's structure and in the way it produced seed.

Among the study group participants was one Dr Dietrich Boie, who had a medical practice in Marburg. He was very enthusiastic about this work. Dietrich Boie was in the process of developing a new treatment for cancer. He felt these potency trials were very important and so asked Maria Thun to work with him and become part of his research team. Another member of the new team was Theodor Schwenk (author of *Sensitive Chaos*) whose extensive research into water and the flow of water led him to develop a machine for improving water. Through working together with Dietrich Boie, who later founded the firm Helixor-Heilmittel, Maria Thun developed an interest in mistletoe research, an interest that remained with her till the end of her life.

Helixor produced and tested the first mistletoe preparation. It became the first mistletoe-based cancer treatment to be officially recognised as such in Germany.

We can see how the interest that was first awakened by her godmother grew throughout Maria Thun's life. This development was of course only possible as the result of her research. Without it and the help of the spiritual world, the successful production of an anthroposophically-inspired remedy would scarcely have been possible.

Experiences as a Gardener

Wilhelm Volz

Following the withdrawal of the German army on May 20, 1945, we found that 93% of the buildings in Crailsheim, southwest Germany, had been destroyed, the greenhouses and cold frames had no glass and all the ground was covered with glass splinters. Our first task was to repair a small greenhouse using glass salvaged from the wreckage and then try to bring the garden back into production.

Alongside this work I studied anthroposophical texts and attended two introductory courses in biodynamics that were being held in Stuttgart during 1947 and 1948. We worked intensively with compost, making manure compost and creating our own potting soil using composted leaf mould and pine needles. But we couldn't imagine how a heavy feeder like cauliflower could attain its full size through compost alone. The workshops which I attended didn't help me either. I found that fungal problems easily arose if organic manures were sprinkled on the soil.

Franz Rulni was also present at these workshops and he explained to me how his calendar [a predecessor of Maria Thun's calendar] worked. I quickly understood the ascending and descending rhythm of the Moon and soon became known for my weather forecasting. It took me longer to feel at home with the Maria Thun's calendar because it required a greater understanding of astronomy. No sooner had I had grasped it than I had to explain it to a student. At the beginning of the year the sowing dates were marked in the calendar and the quantity of seed required noted. When the sowing date arrived we filled the seed boxes with prepared seed compost.

Thanks to the calendar, whose value in helping to organise the work should not be underestimated, we achieved very good and even seed germination. Pricking out seedlings and preparing produce for market was also improved. We sowed the finer seeds ourselves as well.

The six plant preparations for compost regulate the transformation taking place in the manure and compost pile. This enhanced manure encourages plant growth when it is brought out on to the field and the radiant power of the preparations help to enhance soil activity. This effect may seem weaker today than it once was due to the increasing negative influences in our environment. In other words to achieve the same results as we had 65 years ago, we need to use the preparations more intensively.

To this end Maria and Matthias Thun developed the Barrel Preparation. Günther Count von Finckenstein used it to spray over larger areas and had amazing results. I made myself a trailer for this purpose – two wheels, an axle and a box frame capable of carrying 1000 litres (260 US gal) using a small tractor or a VW Golf. With it I sprayed a level 3-ha (7½ acre) ploughed field which had very poor soil and was intended for a forage crop. After a few years we found that instead of hard clods the soil had developed a fine crumb-like structure.

Another farmer was able to rent two fields because his predecessor had grown maize for so many years in succession that nothing would grow on it any more. He sowed lucerne and grass. In May 2012 about half of it was suffering very badly from drought. I looked at the field without much hope of saving it but went ahead and sprayed it with barrel preparation at the rate of 140 l/ha (15 US gal/acre). Despite there having been virtually no rain the area was green again by August and was ready for cutting in September.

Dr Johannes Fetscher told me of a pest control experience he had in 1990 at Herr Lichtenberg market garden. The peat-based seed compost had been infested with fungus gnat larvae. I went to Dortmund and tried to get more information but Herr Lichtenberg was no longer alive. I visited some other farms. Axel Schulze from Dormagen sold his stunning Gerbera at the wholesale flower market in Cologne. As a gardener he knew about pest control and was able to describe Albert Lichtenberg's approach. Lichtenberg had sprayed horn manure on the afflicted plants on three successive evenings and by so doing managed to keep the fungus gnats from doing too much damage.

My own Gerbera were infected with leaf miners imported with the young plants. These are usually controlled using poisonous sprays. I now tried Lichtenberg's method of spraying stirred horn manure three days in succession at about 8 pm, and was successful. I subsequently discovered that Herr Lichtenberg was a frequent visitor to Maria Thun's home in Dexbach and always returned from there with new ideas and suggestions.

I began working in a similar way. We made teas of yarrow, chamomile, stinging nettle, etc. as recommended by Maria Thun to create the conditions in which beneficial organisms could thrive, and sprayed them both under glass and outside. At the same time I made my own preparations, increased the amount used and made great progress with plant protection. At that time the only insecticide we used was Pirimor, a bee-safe pyrethroid. Even this has now become

A view of the greenhouse [Wilhelm Volz]

unnecessary and has been replaced with an increased use of preparations. In the greenhouses we introduced a crop rotation that included climbing beans, lettuce, tomatoes, radishes and corn salad (lamb's lettuce) along with carnations, freesias, chrysanthemums and early summer flowers (antirrhinum, sweet peas, stocks). Fumigation became unnecessary.

In my garden at home (500 m², 600 sq yds) I grow strawberries, raspberries, blackberries, pears, plums, cherries and apples. The variety of apple is Topaz, grown on type 9 rootstock from which we harvest large and beautiful fruit whose flavour exceeds that of the organic Topaz apples from Eppan in South Tirol. Likewise the carrots, beetroot, lettuce, kohlrabi, broccoli and especially potatoes have a much improved taste. Such an improvement in the flavour of produce is only possible if there is a high humus content in the soil (over 5%) and if the preparations are applied frequently and consistently.

Market gardeners have been encouraged in recent years to keep their own livestock. To my perception this has created a lot more work with little improvement in humus levels to show for it. Of course gardeners must work closely with farmers but they need to devote time to their specific task, namely the preparation of humus for the enhancement of quality and by preparing the soil using compost and plenty of biodynamic preparations. The best way of testing quality for me is via the tongue. No other organic organisation can achieve this level of quality – and the customers are convinced.

Moon diagrams

The diagrams overleaf show for each month the daily position (evenings GMT) of the Moon against the stars and other planets. For viewing in the southern hemisphere, turn the diagrams upside down.

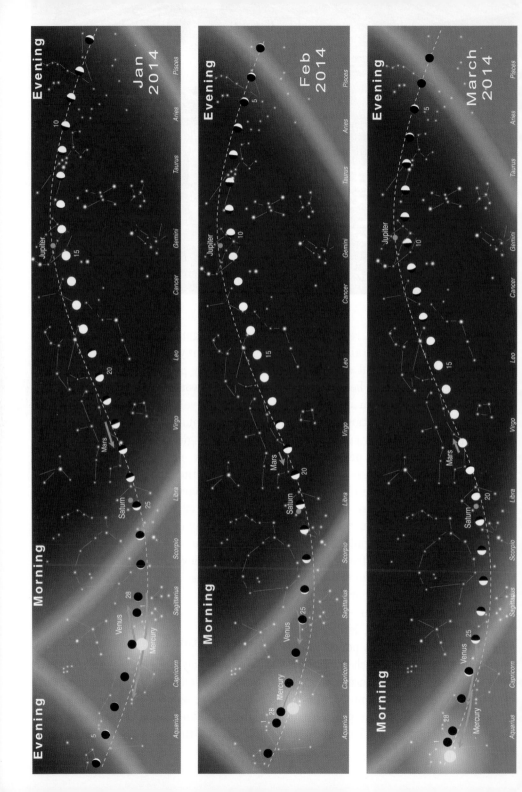

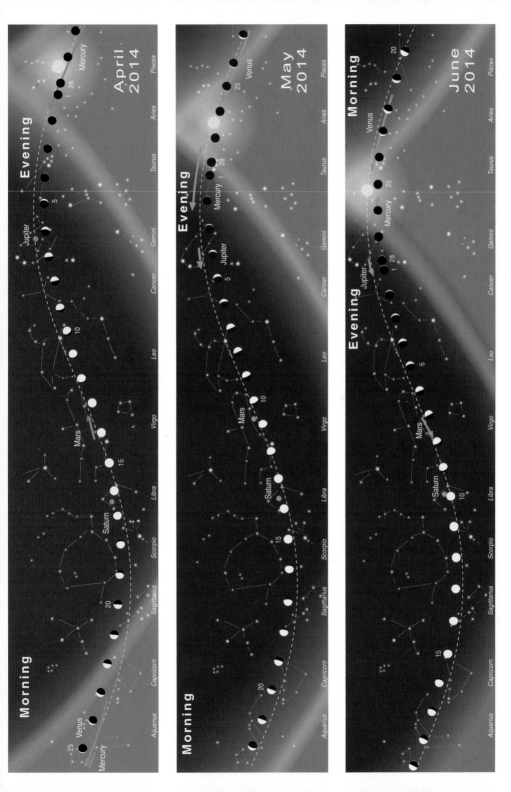

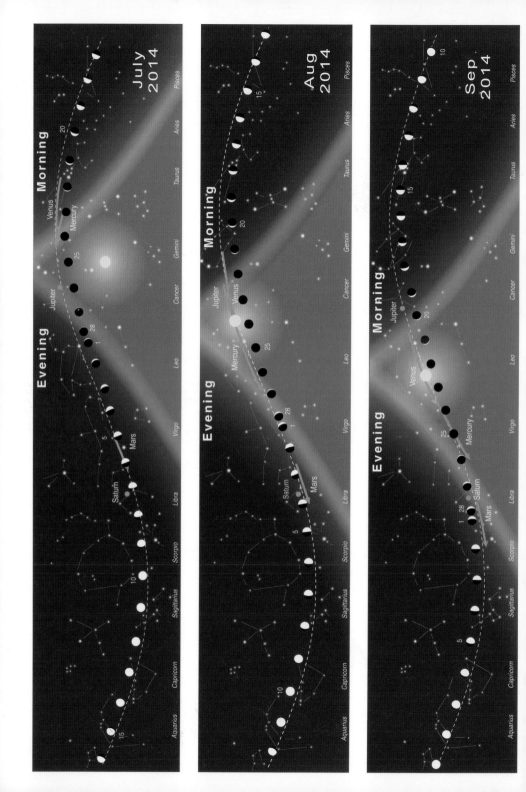

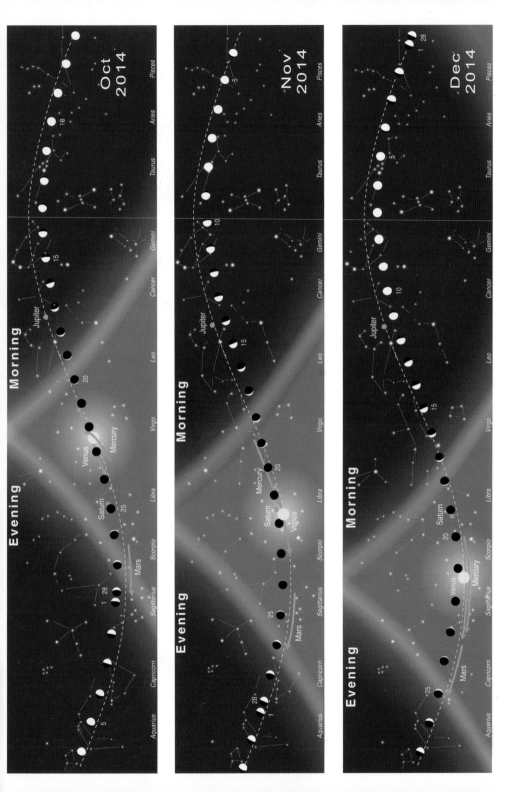

Further reading

Cloos, Walther, *The Living Earth,* Lanthorn.

Colquhoun, Margaret and Axel Ewald, *New Eyes for Plants,* Hawthorn.

Conford, Philip, *The Origins of the Organic Movement,* Floris.

—, *The Development of the Organic Network,* Floris.

Klett, Manfred, *Principles of Biodynamic Spray and Compost Preparations,* Floris.

Koepf, H.H. *The Biodynamic Farm,* Anthroposophic, USA.

—, *Koepf's Practical Biodynamics: Soil, Compost, Sprays and Food Quality,* Floris.

Kranich, Ernst Michael, *Planetary Influences upon Plants,* Biodynamic Literature, USA.

Lepetit, Antoine, *What's so Special About Biodynamic Wine?* Floris.

Masson, Pierre, *The Biodynamic Manual,* Floris.

Osthaus, Karl-Ernst, *The Biodynamic Farm,* Floris.

Pfeiffer, Ehrenfried, *The Earth's Face,* Lanthorn.

—, *Pfeiffer's Introduction to Biodynamics,* Floris.

—, *Soil Fertility, Renewal and Preservation,* Lanthorn.

—, *Weeds and What They Tell Us,* Floris.

—, & Michael Maltas, *The Biodynamic Orchard Book,* Floris.

Philbrick, John and Helen, *Gardening for Health and Nutrition,* Garber, USA.

Schilthuis, Willy, *Biodynamic Agriculture,* Floris.

Soper, John, *Biodynamic Gardening,* Biodynamic Agricultural Ass. UK.

Steiner, Rudolf, *Agriculture (A Course of Eight Lectures),* Biodynamic Literature, USA.

—, *Agriculture: An Introductory Reader,* Steiner Press, UK.

—, *What is Biodynamics? A Way to Heal and Revitalize the Earth,* SteinerBooks, USA.

Storl, Wolf, *Culture and Horticulture,* Biodynamic Farming & Gardening Ass. USA.

Thun, Maria, *Gardening for Life,* Hawthorn.

—, *The Biodynamic Year,* Temple Lodge.

von Keyserlink, Adelbert Count, *The Birth of a New Agriculture,* Temple Lodge.

—, *Developing Biodynamic Agriculture,* Temple Lodge.

Waldin, Monty, *Monty Waldin's Best Biodynamic Wines,* Floris.

Weiler, Michael, *Bees and Honey, from Flower to Jar,* Floris.

Wilkens, J. & Gert Böhm, *Mistletoe Therapy for Cancer,* Floris.

Wright, Hilary, *Biodynamic Gardening for Health and Taste,* Floris.

Biodynamic Associations

Demeter International e.V.
info@demeter.net *www.demeter.net*

Australia: Bio-Dynamic Agricultural Assoc. of Australia, *www.demeter.org.au*
Biodynamic Agricultural Assoc., bdoffice@biodynamics.net.au *www.biodynamics.net.au*

Canada: Society for Bio-Dynamic Farming & Gardening in Ontario, apicanada@gmail.com *www.biodynamics.on.ca*

India: Bio-Dynamic Assoc. of India (BDAI) bdaind@gmail.com *www.biodynamics.in*

Ireland: Biodynamic Agricultural Assoc., bdaai@indigo.ie *www.biodynamic.ie*

New Zealand: Biodynamic Farming & Gardening Assoc., info@biodynamic.org.nz *www.biodynamic.org.nz*

South Africa: Biodynamic Agricultural Assoc. of Southern Africa, info@bdaasa.org.za *www.bdaasa.org.za*

UK: Biodynamic Agricultural Assoc. (BDAA), info@biodynamic.org.uk *www.biodynamic.org.uk*

USA: Biodynamic Farming and Gardening Assoc., info@biodynamics.com *www.biodynamics.com*